[PICTURED LEFT TO RIGHT]

1st row: Cameron, Olivia, Sidney, Seth, and Sam.

2nd row: Zach, Megan, Sean, Sara, Shelli, Sage, and Jason.

3rd row: Tanner, Nate, Jon, Shalae, Sterling, and Shanna.

are as inspiring as handmade cards and scrapbook pages, and each project has special meaning because it comes from you.

We hope you will find something in our catalog to reflect your own unique, personal style so you can share something of yourself with someone else. In the same way, the 2004–2005 Idea Book & Catalog allows us to share Stampin' Up! with you. May you find as much enjoyment in using our products as we did in creating them!

Shelli Gardner

Cofounder and CEO

contents

our stamps

[EASY ASSEMBLY]

In this catalog, you'll find stamp sets you can't find anywhere else! Renowned within the stamping industry, our exclusive images earned the 2004 Creating Keepsakes' Readers' Choice Award for best rubber stamps! Our stamp sets offer the best of both worlds— quality products at a great value. Features include deeply etched images on foam-backed rubber that provide an even imprint while stamping. Our blocks are made of solid maple wood, with side grips that ensure ease of use.

Assembling your stamps is a simple process. We have listed the steps at right for you to follow.

[NOTE] Stamps in the catalog are shown at actual size, making it easy to visualize how they will look on your project. You will also find a list of Stampin' Supplies for each project beginning on page 241.

> STEP 1

Trim the rubber close to the image using the Craft & Rubber scissors (page 225). Make straight cuts instead of curving around the design.

> STEP 2

Match all trimmed rubber images to all appropriate block sizes. Trim and apply labels to the top of the wood blocks.

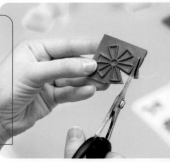

> STEP 3

Peel the paper backing from the stamp, and apply the rubber to the wood block. Be careful to match the position of the rubber with the label on the opposite side.

[VERSATILITY]

Our stamps are sold in sets of coordinating images, which ensures versatility for all of your stamping projects. With each set, you can create cards, scrapbook pages, home décor, gift packaging, and more. Notice the array of projects we have created with the same set, **Shapes & Shadows** (page 63).

Stampin' Up! offers rubber stamps in a variety of styles: bold, line art, contemporary, vintage, and more. With nearly 400 sets in this catalog, there's something to appeal to everyone.

our stamps

[COORDINATION]

With all the images Stampin' Up! offers, you're sure to find countless combinations of stamp sets and products that work together to create a pleasing, consistent feel. These combinations simplify the project-making process—you can choose a theme, select its coordinating products, and plan your project. Here, we present one array of projects that use a fun, funky theme.

When you want to combine stamps from multiple sets or stamps with accessories on one project, look for products with a similar style. You'll be amazed by the incredible looks you can achieve.

Look for these DON'T MISS IT! boxes throughout this catalog for lists of stamp sets and their coordinating accessories, such as Classy Brass® templates and Simply Scrappin® kits.

TRY THESE COORDINATING PRODUCTS: Spring Fling (p. 31), Holiday Basics (p. 46), and It's a Party and Let's Party (p. 87) stamp sets; Dots & Checks background stamp (p. 179); Party Fun wheel (p. 87); Tickles/Pickles Designer Series paper (p. 209); and Party Hat punch (p. 222).

[STAMPIN' AROUND]

If you're looking for an easy way to stamp your projects, nothing's faster than our Stampin' Around® wheels. Because each Stampin' Around wheel is designed to complement images in our stamp sets, you can use the wheel and stamp set together to create beautifully coordinated projects, as we did here with the **Delicate Design** and **Bold Blooms** wheels and **Buds & Blossoms** stamp set (all shown on page 125). With cartridges available in Stampin' Up!'s exclusive colors, wheeled images also coordinate with our other products, such as card stock, eyelets, and more.

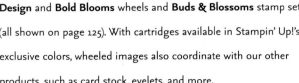

our accessories

Stampin' Up!'s large collection of accessories is based on a foundation of four color families. Because most of our products are formulated to match our 48 colors, we take the guesswork out of color coordination. Each color is organized into one of four families: Bold Brights®, Earth Elements®, Rich Regals®, and Soft Subtles®. The colors within each group are designed to complement each other.

When planning the perfect project, don't underestimate the power of color. Primary colors, like our Bold Brights, make a strong

brilliant blue   gable green   glorious green

green galore   lovely lilac   only orange

orchid opulence   pink passion   positively pink

real red   tempting turquoise   yoyo yellow

BOLD BRIGHTS

EARTH ELEMENTS

basic black   cameo coral   chocolate chip

close to cocoa   creamy caramel   garden green

going gray   more mustard   old olive

really rust   ruby red   summer sun

impression while pastel tones, such as our Soft Subtles, evoke softer thoughts. Use color to convey the mood you want to create.

Once you have selected your color scheme, you have a full range of coordinating products from which to choose—you can spend your time stamping instead of trying to find card stock and accessories that work well together. Decision making is easy!

THESE PRODUCTS AND MORE ARE AVAILABLE IN STAMPIN' UP!'S COLOR FAMILIES:

> Stampin' Write journalers
> Stampin' Write markers*
> Classic Stampin' Pads® and refills*
> Craft Stampin' Pads and refills*
> 8-1/2 x 11 card stock*
> 12 x 12 card stock*
> Stampin' Pastels and refills*

> Stampin' Around cartridges*
> Stampin' Around jumbo cartridges
> Spectrum ink pads (p. 226)
> Round and shaped eyelets (p. 233)
> Tag sheets (p. 219)
> Boxes (p. 219–220)
> Buttons (p. 234)

Products can be found on pages 200–203 unless otherwise noted.
* Available in all 48 colors.

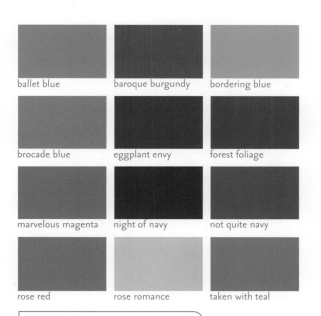

ballet blue	baroque burgundy	bordering blue
brocade blue	eggplant envy	forest foliage
marvelous magenta	night of navy	not quite navy
rose red	rose romance	taken with teal

RICH REGALS

SOFT SUBTLES

almost amethyst	barely banana	bliss blue
blush blossom	lavender lace	mauve mist
mellow moss	mint melody	pale plum
perfect plum	pretty in pink	sage shadow

Just because I care!

for my friend

thanks

how to use our products

[CARDS & GIFT PACKAGING]

Nothing says "I care" more than a handmade greeting or gift. The extra effort you put into your creations will touch the heart of someone you love. Start with a stamp set appropriate for the occasion, select a color scheme, and you are on the road to creating a one-of-a-kind gift with sentimental value. Consider creating a stamped gift along with a coordinating card and packaging. Or make a gift of several stamped cards; simply tie a ribbon around them and attach a beautiful tag as the finishing touch.

Whatever project you envision, Stampin' Up!'s stamp sets and accessories provide you with the supplies necessary to transform your creations from the ordinary to the extraordinary. Whether you're creating cards or three-dimensional items, you'll find everything you need to make your projects truly unique and memorable.

If you are running a little short on creativity, this Idea Book & Catalog includes more than 500 full-color samples of cards, boxes, scrapbook pages, and other projects that you can duplicate.

TRY THIS! Our buttons are hand dyed, and some of the color can be removed with a sanding block for a distressed look.

TRY THIS! Look for these boxes throughout the catalog for helpful hints and tips, including descriptions of stamping techniques shown on some of the samples.

how to use our products

[STAMPIN' MEMORIES]

You may not realize it now, but your friends and family will be forever grateful to you for preserving your memories. Photos capture the images, but they may be meaningless without the stories that go along with them. Explore the variety of options Stampin' Up! provides to help you capture any theme or occasion and preserve your memories of a lifetime so that your family will enjoy reminiscing and poring over your albums in the future.

Our stamps allow you to create custom background papers in colors that enhance your photos. Our alphabet sets provide the chance to stamp perfect titles for your pages. You'll also love our Designer albums, Designer Series papers, and Simply Scrappin' kits, all of which feature Stampin' Up!—exclusive art and are designed to coordinate with our stamps.

Scrapbookers of all skill levels will appreciate the simplicity of our coordinating scrapbook necessities. Many of the products in this catalog are exclusive to Stampin' Up!, which means your pages will always be original and unique! Here's a small sampling of our scrapbooking products:

> Albums (8-1/2 x 11, 12 x 12, and 6 x 6, in ring and post styles) (p. 210–211)
> Simply Scrappin' kits (p. 212–215)
> Write Me a Memory™ Journaling Fonts CDs (p. 198)
> Designer Series papers (12 x 12) (p. 208–209)

> Alphabet stamp sets (p. 195–198)
> Stampin' Write journalers (p. 201–203)
> Tag Sheets (p. 219)
> Vellum (p. 205)
> Round and shaped eyelets (p. 233)
> Fancy Fibers (p. 235)
> Buttons (p. 234)

sm While most of Stampin' Up!'s products are safe for your scrapbooks, our Stampin' Memories symbol clearly marks those that were specifically created for and are the best choice for scrapbooking.

how to use our products

[DEFINITELY DECORATIVE]

Do a little decorating with Definitely Decorative® stamping, and create unique, personalized home décor. Stampin' Up!'s stamp sets are a cost-effective way to revitalize your furniture or coordinate accessories, such as frames, lampshades, dishtowels, etc., to give your room an entirely new look. You can even stamp on walls! And when you're done, you can use these bold stamps to create scrapbook pages, cards, and more.

[TWO-STEP STAMPIN']

Create a single multicolored image with Two-Step Stampin'®— simply layer one image over another for fast and easy stamping with amazing results. Watch for the Two-Step Stampin' logo throughout the catalog for an assortment of images that will spark your imagination.

> STEP 1

Stamp the base image with a light color of ink.

> STEP 2

Stamp the corresponding detail image with a darker ink color.

hostess plan

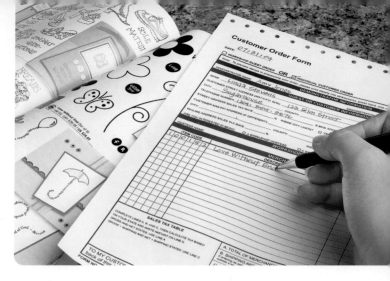

hostess plan

Stampin' Up! offers a generous hostess plan to thank hostesses who open up their homes to us by holding a Stampin' Up! workshop. When you invite friends and family over for an exciting and informative stamping demonstration, you'll also—

> Experience a fun time with people you enjoy.
> Learn different stamping techniques.
> See new project ideas.
> Receive a free Idea Book & Catalog from your demonstrator.
> Earn exclusive hostess sets.
> Earn free Stampin' Up! products based on your workshop's total net sales. (See chart for complete details.)

Ask your Stampin' Up! demonstrator how you can earn the current Hostess Appreciation Special in addition to the products you earn through our hostess plan. Then schedule a workshop, and start earning your free Stampin' Up! products!

[HOSTESS BENEFITS]

net workshop total	hostess sets			hostess awards
	LEVEL 1	LEVEL 2	LEVEL 3	free merchandise totaling up to:
$150.00 – $199.99	choose 1	—	—	$15.00
$200.00 – $249.99	choose 1	—	—	$20.00
$250.00 – $299.99	choose 1	—	—	$25.00
$300.00 – $349.99	choose 1 OR choose 1		—	$35.00
$350.00 – $399.99	choose 1 OR choose 1		—	$40.00
$400.00 – $449.99	choose 1 OR choose 1		—	$45.00
$450.00 – $499.99	choose 1 OR choose 1		—	$50.00
$500.00 – $549.99	choose 2	—	—	$60.00
	OR			
	choose 1	choose 1	—	
	OR			
	—	—	choose 1	
$550.00 – $599.99	choose 2	—	—	$65.00
	OR			
	choose 1	choose 1	—	
	OR			
	—	—	choose 1	
$600.00 – $649.99	choose 2	—	—	$75.00
	OR			
	choose 1	choose 1	—	
	OR			
	—	—	choose 1	
$650.00 – $699.99	choose 2	—	—	$85.00
	OR			
	choose 1	choose 1	—	
	OR			
	—	—	choose 1	
$700.00 – $749.99	choose 2	—	—	$95.00
	OR			
	choose 1	choose 1	—	
	OR			
	—	—	choose 1	
$750.00 +	choose 2	—	—	$100.00 plus 15% of amount over $750.00
	OR			
	choose 1	choose 1	—	
	OR			
	—	—	choose 1	

No shipping and handling amounts are charged on hostess benefits.

  happy
birthday
today-
happy
times
all
year!

happy
birthday
today-
happy
times
all
year!

LEVEL 1 **Birthday Best**
104006 [Set of 4]

Thank You

LEVEL 1 **Stippled Stencils**
104010 [Set of 4]

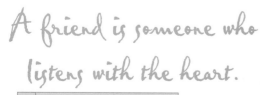

A friend is someone who listens with the heart.

LEVEL 1 **Listen with the Heart**
104026 [Set of 2]

winter
winter
winter

LEVEL 1 **Festive Four**
104053 [Set of 4]

LEVEL 1 **Wee Watercolors**
104075 [Set of 6]

congrats

AunT Ava

Ava, John, Lois
1944

LEVEL 1 **Sculpted Style**
104169 [Set of 4]

i love you more!

Burst into Bloom
104233 [Set of 4]

MYRTLE BEACH

Last year Brianna asked if we could take her to the beach for spring break. We spent four wonderful, sunny days at Myrtle Beach. The weather was perfect. Brianna loved playing on the beach, jet-skiing, kayaking, and enjoying the waves. These pictures were taken our last day there.

April 2003

3 sheets   3 sheets   2 sheets

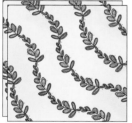

Simply Scrappin'® **In Full Bloom**
104362

Simply Scrappin' kits contain 18 sheets of coordinating materials to create quick and easy, yet distinctive scrapbook pages. Combine with Stampin' Up!'s alphabet stamp sets for personalized page titles. See pages 212–215 for our full line of Simply Scrappin' kits.

hostess plan

that was so sweet of you!

special thoughts

for a special friend

for a special friend

LEVEL 2
Sweet of You
104071 [Set of 6]

to Someone Special

for you

LOvE

that was so sweet of you!

LEVEL 2
Flower Garden
104203 [Set of 7]

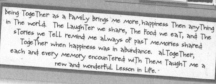

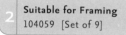

being TogeTher as a FaMiLy brings me More, happiness Then anyThing in The world. The LaughTer we share, The Food we eaT, and The sTories we TeLL remind me always of pasT Memories shared TogeTher when happiness was in abundance. alTogeTher, each and every Memory encounTered wiTh Them TaughT me a new and wonderful Lesson in Life.

LEVEL
2

Suitable for Framing
104059 [Set of 9]

summer party

LEVEL 2   **Botanical Garden**
104051 [Set of 3]

We went to visit grandma and grandpa for a few weeks. The girls had never been to Connecticut and they had not seen grandma and grandpa in over a year. Megan and Jane were a little sad when we had to go.

September 2003

LEVEL 2   **Little Layers Plus**
104055 [Set of 8]

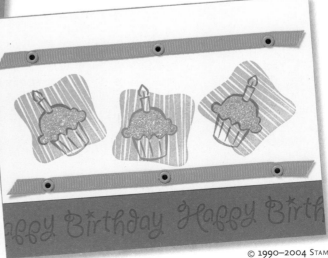

a little something

CELEBRATE!

GOOD LUCK

A NOTE OF THANKS A NOTE OF THANKS A NOTE OF THANKS A NOTE OF THANKS

best witches!

CELEBRATE!

happy shower!

baby

TO:

FROM:

BE MINE BE MINE BE MINE BE MINE BE MINE BE MINE

too cute!

too cute!

DON'T MISS IT! These stamps are sized to fit on our tag sheets, shown on page 219.

LEVEL 3

Tag Time
104107 [Set of 14]

It is Christmas in the heart
that puts Christmas
in the air.
W.T. Ellis

How beautiful a day can be
when friendship touches it.

The greatest
achievements
were at first,
and for some time,
dreams.
-James Allen

The greatest
achievements
were at first,
and for some time,
dreams.
-James Allen

LEVEL

3 **Ageless Adornment**
104049 [Set of 7]

WHaT CouLD Be BeTTeR THan...

HappY HeLLo

WHaT CouLD Be BeTTeR THan...

this?

WHaT couLD Be BeTTeR
THan spenDing a BeauTiFuL
aFTernoon aT The Park?
GeTTinG To spenD iT WiTH
DaDDY! craSe anD DaviD,
summer 2003

LEVEL 3

What Could Be Better?
104217 [Set of 10]

getting started

It's easier than ever to start stamping with these preselected kits of basic stamping supplies. Each kit includes the products you need to make the samples shown here, plus dozens more of your own design!

You can expand your creative options by adding any of the Step It Up items, which offer other products and accessories that will enhance your stamping projects.

ALL NATURAL STAMPIN' KIT

104586   All Natural Stampin' Kit $54.65

(p. 103) All Natural Stamp Set

(p. 204) Confetti Cream Card Stock (8-1/2 x 11)

(p. 206) Confetti Cream Envelopes (Medium)

(p. 202) Assorted Earth Elements Card Stock (8-1/2 x 11)

(p. 202) Really Rust Classic Stampin' Pad

(p. 202) Old Olive Classic Stampin' Pad

(p. 202) More Mustard Classic Stampin' Pad

LITTLE HELLOS STAMPIN' KIT

104587   Little Hellos Stampin' Kit $49.25

(p. 81)   Little Hellos Stamp Set

(p. 204) Ultrasmooth White Card Stock (8-1/2 x 11)

(p. 206) Ultrasmooth White Envelopes (Medium)

(p. 202) Assorted Soft Subtles Card Stock (8-1/2 x 11)

(p. 202) Basic Black Classic Stampin' Pad

(p. 203) Mellow Moss Classic Stampin' Pad

[STEP IT UP]

Earth Elements Buttons
103978 **$6.95** (p. 234)

Natural Hemp Twine
100982 **$2.50** (p. 235)

[STEP IT UP]

Stampin' Pastels
102516 **$24.95** (p. 201)

Blender Pens
102845 **$9.95** (p. 227)

NOTE: We are unable to provide substitutions in these kits, but by using our recommendations as a guideline, you may create "kits" of your own by ordering the items individually. We have provided page numbers for your convenience in selecting the accessories. The bottom sample shown for each kit uses Step It Up products as well as kit items.

© 1990–2004 STAMPIN' UP!

WORD PLAY STAMPIN' KIT

104588   **Word Play** Stampin' Kit $49.25

(p. 191)   Word Play Stamp Set

(p. 204)   Ultrasmooth White Card Stock (8-1/2 x 11)

(p. 206)   Ultrasmooth White Envelopes (Medium)

(p. 202)   Assorted Bold Brights Card Stock (8-1/2 x 11)

(p. 202)   Only Orange Classic Stampin' Pad

(p. 202)   Positively Pink Classic Stampin' Pad

ALL THE BEST STAMPIN' KIT

104589   **All the Best** Stampin' Kit $49.25

(p. 103)   All the Best Stamp Set

(p. 204)   Ultrasmooth Vanilla Card Stock (8-1/2 x 11)

(p. 206)   Ultrasmooth Vanilla Envelopes (Medium)

(p. 202)   Assorted Earth Elements Card Stock (8-1/2 x 11)

(p. 202)   Old Olive Classic Stampin' Pad

(p. 202)   Ruby Red Classic Stampin' Pad

[STEP IT UP]

Bold Brights Eyelets II   Eyelet Tool Kit

100376   **$5.95** (p. 233)   101016   **$7.95** (p. 233)

[STEP IT UP]

Stampin' Write Markers

Basic Black

100082   **$2.95** (p. 202)

More Mustard

100076   **$2.95** (p. 202)

Really Rust   Earths Fancy Fibers

100073   **$2.95** (p. 202)   100396   **$6.95** (p. 235)

VINTAGE STAMPIN' MEMORIES KIT

104585	**Vintage** Stampin' Memories Kit	$63.80

(p. 195) Classic Double Alphabet Stamp Set

(p. 215) Vintage Keepsakes Simply Scrappin' Kit

(p. 202) Creamy Caramel Craft Stampin' Pad

(p. 202) Black Stampin' Write Journaler

[STEP IT UP]

TRY THIS! Use sanding blocks to add an aged look to background paper and stamped images.

Basic Eyelets
100377 **$5.95** (p. 233)

Eyelet Tool Kit
101016 **$7.95** (p. 233)

Sanding Blocks
103301 **$3.50** (p. 217)

Stampin' Dimensionals
104430 **$3.95** (p. 224)

Cream Grosgrain Ribbon
100455 **$5.95** (p. 236)

Silver Brads
104336 **$6.95** (p. 234)

Pecan Classic Leather Album,
available in 3 sizes (p. 210)

PURE & SIMPLE STAMPIN' MEMORIES KIT

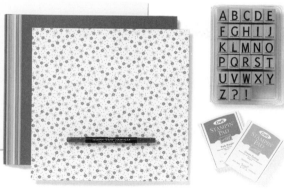

104584	**Pure & Simple** Stampin' Memories Kit	$63.65

(p. 198)   Pure & Simple Alphabet Upper Stamp Set

(p. 204)   Ultrasmooth White Card Stock (12 x 12)

(p. 202)   Assorted Bold Brights Card Stock (12 x 12)

(p. 208)   Sassy Designer Series Paper

(p. 202)   Pink Passion Craft Stampin' Pad

(p. 202)   Green Galore Craft Stampin' Pad

(p. 202)   Real Red Stampin' Write Journaler

[STEP IT UP]

Silver Brads
104336   **$6.95**   (p. 234)

Red Grosgrain Ribbon
102682   **$5.95**   (p. 236)

1/8-inch Circle Punch
100391   **$8.95**   (p. 222)

Buds & Blossoms Stamp Set
103633   **$19.95**   (p. 125)

Sassy Designer Series Vellum
103653   **$9.95**   (p. 208)

Groovy Lines Designer Album,
available in 3 sizes   (p. 210)

Aluminum Metal Edge Tags (White Circle)
103374   **$3.95**   (p. 218)

BE
MINE

KISS
ME

LOVE
YOU

HUGS

Sweet Talk [Set of 6]
103967 **$9.95**

True Love [Set of 6]
100188 **$16.95**

103795 Stampin' Around® **Hearts & Flowers** **$5.95** (Wheel only. Handle and ink cartridges sold separately. See pages 202–203, 228.)

102254 Stampin' Around® **Love Swirls** **$5.95** (Wheel only. Handle and ink cartridges sold separately. See pages 202–203, 228.)

Loving Hearts [Set of 7]
103728 **$19.95**

Smitten [Set of 6]
103883 **$17.95**

104069 Stampin' Around® **All Heart** **$5.95** (Wheel only. Handle and ink cartridges sold separately. See pages See pages 202–203, 228.)

Have a Heart [Set of 7]
101999 **$19.95**

Happy Hearts [Set of 6]
100319 **$14.95**

102596 Stampin' Around® **Hugs & Kisses** **$5.95** (Wheel only. Handle and ink cartridges sold separately. See pages See pages 202–203, 228.)

This was Ashley's first Easter. She loved collecting all the brightly colored plastic eggs. Ashley liked the blue ones the best. She loved the sound they made when she shook them; but as soon as she discovered the candy inside; that is all she wanted.

HAPPY SPRING!

Spring Fling [Set of 4]
104020 **$11.95**

DON'T MISS IT! The Spring Fling set coordinates with the Groovy Lines background stamp on page 180.

Kiss me, I'm Irish!

Hearts & Clovers [Set of 6]
100382 **$14.95**

Easter Blessings

I am the resurrection, and the life: he that believeth in me, though he were dead, yet shall he live...

John 11:25

Renewed Faith [Set of 4]
100317 **$17.95**

Wishing you and those you love renewed faith and hope in Christ.

Wishing you all the lovely gifts of spring!

Spring Gifts [Set of 6]
102507 **$19.95**

102291 Stampin' Around® **Spring Things** **$5.95** (Wheel only. Handle and ink cartridges sold separately. See pages 202–203, 228.)

MAY YOUR HALLOWEEN BE FULL OF SMILES!

Halloween Smiles [Set of 4]
100136 **$18.95**

trick or treat

sam may not look as happy as most clowns, but he's certainly the sweetest one! This halloween was especially fun because family from several states arrived at the ritz carlton early afternoon for trick-or-treating from room to room, pizza, treats, bobbing for apples, and dancing in a spooky ballroom. The kids didn't want the evening to end, and it was so nice for the adults to watch and to visit with everyone... anticipation of chelsea's wedding the next...

october 2003

you make me smile!

Carved & Candlelit [Set of 6]
104225 **$14.95**

TRICK OR TREAT

Trick or Treat [Set of 4]
100028 **$11.95**

TRY THIS! For best results, cut the Magic Mesh so that it is slightly larger than the card stock you want to cover. Then trim the edges.

Happy Halloween

BE AFRAID!
be very afraid

The boys wanted to be scary this Halloween. Matthew bought a "Scream" mask and used an old cape from a previous Halloween. Jeremy wanted to be something like the Nazgul from "The Lord of the Rings". I took a black robe and added material to the sleeves and tore it, then made a hood with a screen in it. He was excited about it. Chase wanted to be a skeleton, so I appliquéd felt "bones" to a black sweat suit. Three scary boys on the loose!

Bitty Boos [Set of 12]
104461 **$16.95**

100267 Stampin' Around® **Happy Jacks** $5.95 (Wheel only. Handle and ink cartridges sold separately. See pages 202–203, 228.)

no trick
-or-
treater
could ever
be
Sweeter!

halloween 2003

no
trick
-or-
treater
could ever
be
sweeter!

you're
invited

Sweeter Treaters [Set of 8]
103530 **$21.95**

Halloween Backgrounds [Set of 4]
104028 **$11.95**

100351 Stampin' Around® **Spooky Spiders** **$5.95** (Wheel only. Handle and ink cartridges sold separately. See pages 202–203, 228.)

Happy Passover

Mazel Tov on your Bat Mitzvah

Mazel Tov on your Marriage

Mazel Tov on your Bar Mitzvah

Happy Rosh Hashanah

Rosh Hashanah

Mazel Tov [Set of 6]
100329 **$19.95**

Hanukkah

Happy Hanukkah

TRY THIS! When using our die-cut boxes, lightly sand the edges of the box after punching it out of the sheet to create a smooth edge. The die-cut box shown at right is sold on page 219.

Festive Hanukkah [Set of 4]
100347 **$16.95**

© 2003 STAMPIN' UP!

Happy Holidays

sending
a little
wish
for a lot
of joy!

Have yourself a merry little Christmas!

Little Holiday Wishes [Set of 12]
104462 **$16.95**

wishing you sweet holiday memories

Happy Holidays

HOLIDAY JOY

Wishing you sweet holiday memories

Christopher and Jacob love the holidays. They spend a lot of time at Grandma & Grandpa's house when Mom & Dad go shopping.
December 2003

Sweet Holidays [Set of 6]
104032 **$16.95**

104157 Stampin' Around® **Holiday Sweets** **$5.95** (Wheel only. Handle and ink cartridges sold separately. See pages 202–203, 228.)

Happy Holidays

TRY THIS! Use the Metal Edge tags with any color of card stock by cutting out the center of the tag with a hobby blade, removing the existing piece, and glueing a slightly larger piece in the color of your choice to the back of the tag.

Frosty [Set of 4]
101826 **$16.95**

merry & bright · ho! ho! ho! · 'tis the season · joy · deck the halls

Crazy for Christmas [Set of 4]
100126 **$19.95**

103150 Stampin' Around® **Heart Angels** **$5.95** (Wheel only. Handle and ink cartridges sold separately. See pages 202–203, 228.)

DON'T MISS IT! The font in this set coordinates with the Casual font on the Write Me a Memory® Journaling Font CD, Volume I sold on page 198. Use the CD to add a personal touch to your projects.

'Tis The season·celebrate·joy
deck The halls·happy holidays
jingle all The way·holly jolly
peace on earTh·Fa La La La La
merry and brighT·LeT iT snow
joy·happy chrisTmas·misTLeToe
warmesT holiday wishes·noel
home For chrisTmas·ho ho ho

holidays

St nicholas

good sT. nick has come To our house To sTay. he has rosy cheeks and a LiTTLe round belly so we know he's The real Thing. chrisTmas has Taken on a whole new meaning This year wiTh our FirsT child in The house. we have much To be Thank-Ful For. chrisTmas 2002

nicholas TrenT Thompson chrisTmas 2002

Yule Bits & Borders [Set of 8]
103871 **$24.95**

be merry

may your merry be very!

Very Merry [Set of 4]
104484 **$11.95**

Season's Sketches [Set of 8]
100674 **$28.95**

to:

from:

happy holidays

Holiday Woodcuts [Set of 6]
100006 **$19.95**

103161 Stampin' Around® **Christmas Time** **$5.95** (Wheel only. Handle and ink cartridges sold separately. See pages 202–203, 228.)

MERRY CHRISTMAS!

NO PEEKING 'TIL CHRISTMAS!

HAPPY HOLLY-DAYS!

TO: FROM:

JOY

HO! HO! HO!

Holiday Sampler [Set of 28]
104463 **$29.95**

HOPE YOUR HOLIDAY SPARKLES WITH HAPPINESS!

Sparkling Season [Set of 6]
100335 **$19.95**

DON'T MISS IT! This set has a coordinating Simply Scrappin'® kit sold on page 215.

Theodore
chrisTmas '03

100398 Stampin' Around® **Candy Cane Craze** **$5.95** (Wheel only. Handle and ink cartridges sold separately. See pages 202–203, 228.)

HAPPY HO-HO-HOLIDAYS!

Ho-Ho-Holidays [Set of 6]
100142 **$17.95**

HAPPY HO-HO-HOLIDAYS!

To: Joellyn
From: Abby

Happy Holidays!

Some of my best friends are flakes!

Happy Holidays!

Flaky Friends [Set of 8]
101850 **$24.95**

100417 Stampin' Around® **Many Mittens** $5.95 (Wheel only. Handle and ink cartridges sold separately. See pages 202–203, 228.)

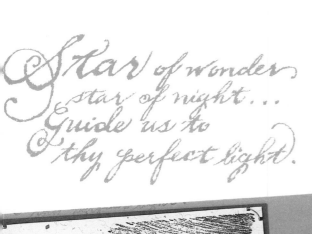

Star of Wonder [Set of 2]
100253 **$17.95**

Holiday Print [Set of 1]
100313 **$16.95**

101927 Stampin' Around® **Snowman Fun** **$5.95** (Wheel only. Handle and ink cartridges sold separately. See pages 202–203, 228.)

Happy Winter

Happy Winter [Set of 4]
100789 **$11.95**

LeT iT snow!

Love

Friendship is... the sort of love one can imagine between Angels.

wishing you a Season of peace

Angelic [Set of 6]
100261 **$28.95**

TRY THIS! The Tearing Edge (sold on page 225) produces a perfectly torn edge every time as shown on the card above. Simply press one hand firmly on the metal while pulling the card stock toward you with the other hand.

101638 Stampin' Around® **Star** **$5.95** (Wheel only. Handle and ink cartridges sold separately. See pages 202–203, 228.)

May Christmas fill your heart with a warm and friendly light.

To:
From:

May Christmas fill your heart with a warm and friendly light.

Sleigh Ride [Set of 6]
100176 **$21.95**

Warmest Holiday Wishes

To:
From:

may the spirit of Love, the beauty of Hope and the blessings of Peace be your gifts this Christmas Season

Holiday Wishes [Set of 6]
100426 **$22.95**

103195 Stampin' Around® **Gifts Galore** **$5.95** (Wheel only. Handle and ink cartridges sold separately. See pages 202–203, 228.)

MERRY *Christmas*

Christmas Foliage [Set of 9]
100122 **$28.95**

Holiday Basics [Set of 3]
100110 **$17.95**

104102 Stampin' Around® **Funky Firs** **$5.95** (Wheel only. Handle and ink cartridges sold separately. See pages 202–203, 228.)

Wishing you all the magic and wonder the season brings

Magic & Wonder [Set of 2]
103816 **$17.95**

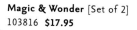

May the holiday spirit find a home in your heart.

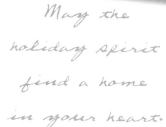

Holiday Spirit [Set of 6]
103532 **$19.95**

103543 Stampin' Around® **Only Ornaments** **$5.95** (Wheel only. Handle and ink cartridges sold separately. See pages 202–203, 228.)

To:
From:

To:
From:

To: mary jane
From: amy

To: Jennifer
From: Mike

To:
From:

DO NOT OPEN 'TIL CHRISTMAS!

To:
From:

To:
From:

To:
From:

To:
From:

DO NOT OPEN 'TIL CHRISTMAS!

Christmas Gift Tags [Set of 8]
101920 **$26.95**

101829 Stampin' Around® **Gingerbread Man** **$5.95** (Wheel only. Handle and ink cartridges sold separately. See pages 202–203, 228.)

103296 Stampin' Around® **Candy Cane Christmas** **$5.95** (Wheel only. Handle and ink cartridges sold separately. See pages 202–203, 228.)

Snowy Play [Set of 4]
100341 **$18.95**

Lace Snowflakes [Set of 4]
101487 **$14.95**

winter wonderland

The fifth day of our New England trip was spent in Vermont. There had been an ice storm the day before and the trees were coated with ice. The road to the Smith Family Farm looked like a scene from an old movie. November 2002.

101233 Stampin' Around® **Snowflake** $5.95 (Wheel only. Handle and ink cartridges sold separately. See pages 202–203, 228.)

May the quiet beauty of this season bring you deep joy and warm memories to cherish throughout the coming year.

May the quiet beauty of this season bring you deep joy and warm memories to cherish throughout the coming year.

A Beautiful Season [Set of 6]
100158 **$28.95**

101088 Stampin' Around® **Pine Bough** **$5.95** (Wheel only. Handle and ink cartridges sold separately. See pages 202–203, 228.)

Warm Winter Wishes

Snowflakes [Set of 6]
101589 **$21.95**

TRY THIS! The Powder Pal on page 230 provides the perfect complement to embossing. Use it to catch the excess embossing powder and funnel it back into its container.

The world in solemn stillness lay...

May the beauty of the season bring you joy and warm memories to cherish throughout the year.

The world in solemn stillness lay...

Solemn Stillness [Set of 6]
103771 **$28.95**

104061 Stampin' Around® **Star Studded** **$5.95** (Wheel only. Handle and ink cartridges sold separately. See pages 202–203, 228.)

Hoping your day
is filled with happiness!

Spring is
nature's way
of saying~
"Let's party"!

Hoping your day
is filled with happiness!

Spring Party [Set of 6]
102601 **$21.95**

Just because I care!

Simply Spring [Set of 8]
103298 **$21.95**

DON'T MISS IT! This set has a coordinating Classy Brass®
embossing template sold on page 231.

102005 Stampin' Around® **Joy of Spring** **$5.95** (Wheel only. Handle and ink cartridges sold separately. See pages 202–203, 228.)

100811 Stampin' Around® **Busy Bees** **$5.95** (Wheel only. Handle and ink cartridges sold separately. See pages 202–203, 228.)

Joy is not
in things,
it is in us.
–Richard Wagner

Wishing
you
happiness.

Summer by the Sea [Set of 6]
104243 **$28.95**

DON'T MISS IT! This set has a coordinating
Simply Scrappin® kit sold on page 214.

TRY THIS! Ink refills are great for
watercoloring. Simply use a few drops from
the ink refills, diluted with water. Apply with a
watercolor brush.

My LiTTle Meg,

My dreams for you are many:

ThaT you find joy in all of Life's
blessings

ThaT you make The best ouT of
every experience Life brings your way

ThaT you always maintain your
faiTh and hold sTrong To your
convictions

ThaT you will find a man To spend
your Life wiTh ThaT is as wonderful
as your daddy

ThaT you treasure and hold on To
your good friends

ThaT you are able To find joy wiThin
yourself, always

I am so blessed To have you
Life. your spirit and fun-Loving
naTure bring so much warmTh
happiness To our family.

Meagan anne
summer 2003

The best things
in life
are not free,
but priceless.

Love returned
is the
true reward
of love given.

The best things
in life
are not free,
but priceless.

i miss you

DON'T MISS IT! This set has a coordinating
Simply Scrappin® kit sold on page 214.

Seaside Sketches [Set of 6]
103555 **$27.95**

On the Beach [Set of 13]
101417 **$26.95**

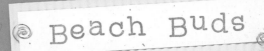

Beach Buds

since we started going to the beach every saturday, emma and cody have really become great friends. They love to build sand castles and collect sea shells, but most of all They enjoy splashing around in The cold water.

summer 2003

Just because I care!

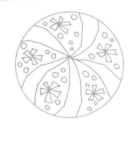

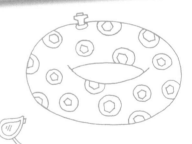

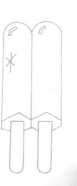

Sparkling Summer [Set of 11]
104163 **$24.95**

TRY THIS! When used with glitter and Pearl Ex as shown above, Crystal Effects (sold on page 232) can be an adhesive as well as an embellishment. To re-create the look shown on the card above, apply a very thin coat, add glitter, and enjoy the results!

i Love YOU More!

2 peas in a pod.

our little
Farmer Girl

Kate Lyn
AUG. 03

Kate's favorite part of
summer is harvesting
veggies. She loves to eat them!

Definitely Decorative® **Vegetable Garden** [Set of 10]
100291 **$32.95**

Happy Fall Y'all [Set of 7]
100961 **$19.95**

Fall Whimsy [Set of 6]
100130 **$14.95**

100360 Stampin' Around® **Acorns $5.95** (Wheel only. Handle and ink cartridges sold separately. See pages 202–203, 228.)

Definitely Decorative® **Vine & Berry** [Set of 3]
100192 **$16.95**

Definitely Decorative® **Fancy Foliage** [Set of 4]
100297 **$24.95**

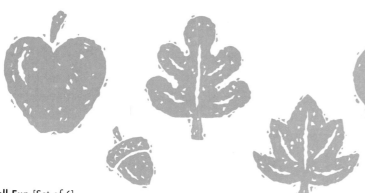

Fall Fun [Set of 6]
100675 **$14.95**

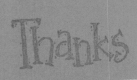

Shawn and I made a visit back to Illinois this fall to visit the home where he grew up. It was a memorable journey full of wonderful stories and good times.

October 2003

journey

Lovely Leaves [Set of 6]
100263 **$28.95**

Changing Seasons [Set of 4]
100120 **$26.95**

thank you

thanks for your kindness

Little Somethings [Set of 12]
101635 **$16.95**

102604 Stampin' Around® **Pindot** **$5.95** (Wheel only. Handle and ink cartridges sold separately. See pages 202–203, 228.)

A Tree for All Seasons [Set of 4]
102744 **$11.95**

Love you

TRY THIS! To get a clean image with a background stamp (as shown on the card at right), set the stamp on a flat surface rubber side up and place the card stock on the inked rubber. Cover with a piece of scratch paper and rub all areas of the stamp, being careful to keep the card stock from sliding.

Sweet Seasons [Set of 4]
104024 **$27.95**

A Year in the Country [Set of 3]
104109 **$17.95**

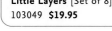

Little Layers [Set of 8]
103049 **$19.95**

101965 Stampin' Around® **Lovely Ladybug**s **$5.95** (Wheel only. Handle and ink cartridges sold separately. See pages 202–203, 228.)

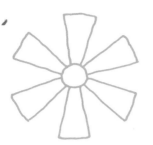

merry &
bright

allison's
10th birthday
may 22, 2003

the 3 amigos
callie · megan
marykate

Shapes & Shadows [Set of 12]
104014 **$29.95**

DON'T MISS IT! See more samples made with
this versatile set on page 3.

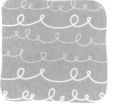

Window on the World [Set of 7]
103941 **$19.95**

Little Layers II [Set of 8]
100030 **$19.95**

Christmas Cutie

May this holiday
find you
surrounded
by those you love.

May this holiday
find you
surrounded
by those you love.

Thanks!

Just a little note
to let you know
how much your
kindness
means to me.

Sketch It [Set of 12]
103311 **$34.95**

© 2001 STAMPIN' UP!

Thanks!
© 2001 STAMPIN' UP!

TRY THIS! Use the strong, double-sided Sticky Strip
adhesive on page 224 to assemble our die-cut boxes.

each day is a gift   *all my love...*

silent night, holy night...   *if life gives you lemons...*

Country Comfort [Set of 4]
104022 **$14.95**

Year-Round Fun II [Set of 28]
103913 **$28.95**

Simple Seasons [Set of 6]
103641 **$14.95**

I want to be you when I grow up!

DON'T MISS IT! This set has a coordinating Classy Brass embossing template sold on page 231.

You take the cake!
HAPPY·BIRTHDAY

PHOTO OP

When Mom jot a Hijh-enD Digital camera For christMas, she took Me to the reFlectinj Pool For a test Photo shoot. i enjoyeD jettinj all slickeD uP For the Pictures, BuT the Best Part was sPenDinj the aFternoon alone with MoM while DaD took care of Jessica. we jijjleD aBouT Me actinj like a New York MoDel & MaDe jooFy Faces aT each other, Then enDeD the Day with a jooD heart-to-heart over a cuP of Hot chocolate. iT was just what i neeDeD to LiJhten the aFter-christMas BLues i was Feelinj.

January 17, 2004

Stipple Celebrations [Set of 14]
104483 **$28.95**

103751 Stampin' Around® Jumbo **Busy Blocks** **$7.95** (Wheel only. Handle and ink cartridges sold separately. See pages 202–203, 228.)

THANK YOU

THANKS SO MUCH

HOORAY FOR YOU!

HAPPY BIRTHDAY

GET WELL SOON

FROM THE HEART

FRIEND·TO·FRIEND

HAPPY BIRTHDAY

HAPPY BIRTHDAY

Nice & Easy Notes [Set of 8]
103039 **$26.95**

Thank You

Happy Birthday

Best Wishes

Thinking of You

Simple Wishes [Set of 4]
101167 **$11.95**

happy everything!

celebrate you!

thank you

just because i care...

thinking of you

happily ever after

happy new baby!

'tis the season

Greetings Galore [Set of 8]
104477 **$28.95**

Bitty Bolds [Set of 12]
104464 **$16.95**

104099 Stampin' Around® **Polka Dot Blocks** **$5.95** (Wheel only. Handle and ink cartridges sold separately. See pages 202–203, 228.)

Happy
Birthday

Happy
Holidays

thank
you!

HONEY

Happy

for you

Favorite Teddy Bear [Set of 15]
103361 **$29.95**

101090 Stampin' Around® **Paw Tracks** **$5.95** (Wheel only. Handle and ink cartridges sold separately. See pages 202–203, 228.)

happy
day

very
merry

little
one

Nice & Narrow [Set of 9]
100160 **$21.95**

TRY THIS! StazOn™ ink is a great choice on our Metal Magic tags. Keep your Stampin' Mist handy— you can wipe off the image if you make a mistake while stamping.

The Fine Print [Set of 6]
100615 **$16.95**

101100 Stampin' Around® **Double-Line Stitched Plaid $5.95** (Wheel only. Handle and ink cartridges sold separately. See pages 202–203, 228.)

thank you thank you tha
you thank you thank yo
nk you thank you thank
ou thank you thank you
ank you thank you thanl
u thank you thank you t

love joy peace love joy p
oy peace love joy peace
ve joy peace love joy pea
peace love joy peace love
ce love joy peace love joy
joy peace love joy peace

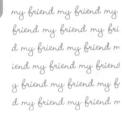

my friend my friend my
friend my friend my fri
d my friend my friend m
iend my friend my friend
y friend my friend my f
d my friend my friend m

elebrate! celebrate! celeb
te! celebrate! celebrate! c
lebrate! celebrate! celebr
rate! celebrate! celebrate
elebrate! celebrate! celeb
! celebrate! celebrate! ce

Celebrating

IN THE FALL OF 2003, WE VISITED THE PETERSEN
FARM. THE GIRLS LOVED CLIMBING THE TALL
LADDERS TO RETRIEVE THE BEAUTIFUL, RIPE, RED
APPLES FROM THE OBLIGING TREES. KATE
THOUGHT IT WOULD BE FUN TO PLAY A LITTLE
HIDE-AND-SEEK. MOM WASN'T TOO THRILLED WHEN
KATE VANISHED IN THE ORCHARD. WE QUICKLY
ASSEMBLED A SEARCH PARTY, AND WITH MEGAN
AND ELIZABETH'S HELP WE WERE ABLE TO FIND
KATE PROPPED BEHIND AN APPLE TREE EATING A
VERY LARGE APPLE AND SINGING A SONG.

THE DAY WAS FILLED WITH PRETEND TRACTOR
RIDES, HORSE RIDES, AND ALL THE APPLES YOU
COULD EAT! WE'LL BE TAKING ANOTHER TRIP TO
THE FARM AGAIN THIS YEAR. LITTLE ANNIE WILL
BE WALKING - AND IT MIGHT JUST BE HER TURN
TO HIDE IN THE ORCHARD.

OCTOBER 2003

KATE, MEGAN, AND ELIZABETH

Fall With
Friends

Mini Messages [Set of 8]
103796 **$16.95**

I LOVE YOU

DON'T MISS IT! This set has a coordinating Classy Brass® embossing template sold on page 231.

Bold Basics [Set of 11]
103178 **$24.95**

to have and to hold / to have and to hold / to have and to hold / to have and to hold

FROM THE HEART FROM THE HEART FROM THE HEART

itsy bitsy baby itsy bitsy baby itsy bitsy baby itsy bitsy baby itsy bitsy baby

good for you! good for you! good for you! good for you! good for you!

just a little something / something just a little / little something just a

happy holidays happy holidays happy holidays happy holidays happy holidays

FROM THE HEART FROM THE HEART FROM THE HEART

Figures of Speech [Set of 8]
103935 **$21.95**

TRY THIS! Figures of Speech and Mini Messages (shown opposite) were both designed to fit perfectly on our Metal Edge tags (page 218).

celebrate you! celebrate you! celebrate you! celebrate you! celebrate you!

thank you thank you thank you thank you thank you thank you thank you thank you

thanks

a little bit of thanks for a whole lot of nice!

birthdays are good for you- the more you have, the longer you live!

your kindness touches my heart.

when it's dark enough, you can see the stars.
-Ralph Waldo Emerson

Quick & Cute [Set of 8]
103236 **$16.95**

Vertical Greetings [Set of 4]
101806 **$19.95**

the perfect pair!

the perfect pair!

kelli & joey

the perfect pair!

Jenkin's cabin
august 2003

miss you

On the Line [Set of 7]
100008 **$19.95**

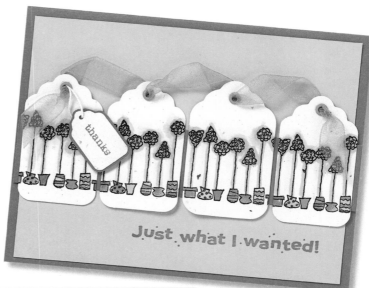

Just what I wanted!

TRY THIS! Available in color families, our tag sheets (page 219) include an assortment of layering tags and duplicate sizes (such as the ones shown here).

Simple Somethings [Set of 4]
104482 **$11.95**

20 **tiny fingers**

Matthew Blake
5 lbs. 12 oz.
17 inches
A perfect 10!
&
Mark Edward
5 lbs. 1 oz.
16 inches
Another perfect 10!

20 **tiny toes**

Just My Type [Set of 7]
100301 **$19.95**

104312 Stampin' Around® **Hot to Dot $5.95** (Wheel only. Handle and ink cartridges sold separately. See pages 202–203, 228.)

You light up my life! Welcome, baby! Hang in there!

Make a wish! Just Because Get well soon! Happy Holidays

Wedding Wishes

Just a note You're sweet!

I'm sorry

 For the Bride

 You did it! For you

Mini Mates [Set of 28]
104465 **$29.95**

Just for You
to: _____
from: _____

Tags & More [Set of 8]
101380 **$19.95**

Happy Birthday

It's a Shower

*Date
Time
Place
For
RSVP*

Something to Celebrate [Set of 9]
104016 **$24.95**

good
times

friends

noel

good luck

surprise!

shop!

dream

celebrate

smile

she's here

he's here

sweet

congrats

joy

Good Times [Set of 28]
104466 **$28.95**

TRY THIS! The designs in our Good Times set are perfectly sized
to use with the Great Shapes set on page 177.

Simply Sweet [Set of 4]
100337 **$19.95**

Sketch an Event [Set of 8]
102032 **$21.95**

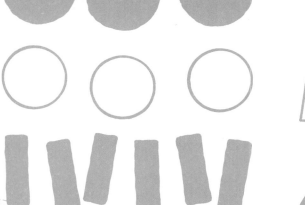

merry & bright

hello

Fun with Shapes [Set of 13]
104040 **$24.95**

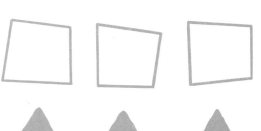

STACY, ALLIE, AND LEXI ARE SO LUCKY TO HAVE EACH OTHER! THE MEDFORD SIDE OF OUR FAMILY GETS TOGETHER EVERY YEAR FOR MEMORIAL DAY, AND THIS YEAR THE GIRLS GOT TO RIDE TOGETHER IN GRANDPA'S CONVERTIBLE RIGHT DOWN MAIN STREET. THEY LOVED WAVING TO THE CROWD AND SMILING FOR THE CAMERAS!

MAY 2003

HELLO!

Simply Circles [Set of 6]
103939 **$17.95**

Thank You

Miss You...

Happy Birthday to You... ♪

hello...

Thinking of You

Best Wishes

Welcome Baby!

To Someone Special...

Feathered Friends [Set of 8]
102680 **$26.95**

Thank You

just a note

hello...

hello...

Thank you

Happy Birthday

Hedgehog Happiness [Set of 6]
101253 **$19.95**

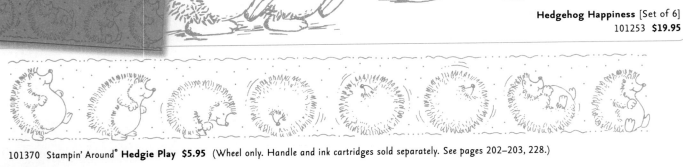

101370 Stampin' Around® **Hedgie Play $5.95** (Wheel only. Handle and ink cartridges sold separately. See pages 202–203, 228.)

thanks for everything!

da dum dee dum...

babies are the best gift of all

happy holidays

pursenally, you're the best!

congratulations!

a birthday wish for my friend... may the happy never end!

finally!

thanks for everything!

Framed Greetings [Set of 14]
104034 **$28.95**

da dum dee dum...

Love

happy birthday

friends

best wishes

miss you

happy holidays

friends

for baby

thank you

thinking of you

friends   friends   friends

Little Hellos [Set of 8]
104478 **$19.95**

DON'T MISS IT! This set is also sold as part of a kit on page 24.

Many Moos [Set of 4]
100154 **$24.95**

Mini Medleys [Set of 12]
104467 **$16.95**

DON'T MISS IT! This set has a coordinating Classy Brass® embossing template sold on page 231.

100941 Stampin' Around® **Easy Check** **$5.95** (Wheel only. Handle and ink cartridges sold separately. See pages 202–203, 228.)

Simple Sketches [Set of 12]
102771 **$28.95**

A Greeting for All Reasons [Set of 14]
100999 **$28.95**

Sketch a Party [Set of 9]
101651 **$24.95**

Perfect Party [Set of 9]
103029 **$24.95**

100354 Stampin' Around® **Bold Celebrate** **$5.95** (Wheel only. Handle and ink cartridges sold separately. See pages 202–203, 228.)

YOU MAKE ME SMILE!

HOPE YOUR DAY IS THE HAPPY-FACE KIND!

HAPPY BIRTHDAY!

Smile [Set of 6]
102654 **$14.95**

a HAPPY HELLO!

WISHING YOU a SEASON OF HAPPY SMILES!

WISHING YOU MANY HAPPY SURPRISES!

a HAPPY HELLO!

Smile Some More [Set of 6]
104057 **$14.95**

Surprise!

Have a Happy Birthday!

Surprise! [Set of 4]
104118 **$14.95**

104063 Stampin' Around® **Splat** **$5.95** (Wheel only. Handle and ink cartridges sold separately. See pages 202–203, 228.)

HAPPY! HAPPY! HAPPY!

BIRTHDAY

Sidney had a fabulous fifth birthday! She invited friends over to dress up, make necklaces, and have delicious raspberry sorbet and cookies. Sidney especially loved being in her dress, with a touch of make up, and a smile to top it off.

HAPPY! HAPPY! HAPPY! HAPPY!

HAPPY! HAPPY! HAPPY!

Polka Dot Party [Set of 11]
103616 **$24.95**

DON'T MISS IT! This set has a coordinating Simply Scrappin'® kit sold on page 213 and a Classy Brass® embossing template sold on page 231.

happy birthday

103750 Stampin' Around® Jumbo **Perfect Polka Dots** $7.95 (Wheel only. Handle and ink cartridges sold separately. See pages 202–203, 228.)

HAPPY·BIRTHDAY!

100552 Stampin' Around® **Happy Birthday** $5.95 (Wheel only. Handle and ink cartridges sold separately. See pages 202–203, 228.)

BIRTHDAY

DATE: April 5th

TIME: 1:00 pm

ace: Am

DATE: HAPPY
BIRTHDAY!

TIME:

PLACE:

FOR:

IT'S a
PARTY!

DON'T MISS IT!
The stamp sets and wheel on this page coordinate with the Dots & Checks and Groovy Lines background stamps on pages 179 and 180.

It's a Party [Set of 6]
103769 **$19.95**

LET'S
PARTY

Let's Party [Set of 4]
100148 **$11.95**

100358 Stampin' Around® Party Fun **$5.95** (Wheel only. Handle and ink cartridges sold separately. See pages 202–203, 228.)

January Carnation

February Violet

March Jonquil

April Sweet Pea

May Lily of the Valley

June Rose

July Larkspur

August Gladiolus

September Aster

October Marigold

November Chrysanthemum

December Narcissus

Flower of the Month [Set of 12]
101084 **$29.95**

TRY THIS! Save your card stock and paper scraps—they make wonderful embellishments.

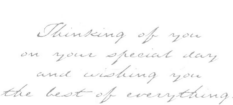

Happy Birthday

Thinking of you on your special day and wishing you the best of everything.

Happy Birthday Frame [Set of 2]
100632 **$11.95**

A great big wish for a fun-filled day!

A great big wish for a fun filled day!

Birthday Bunnies [Set of 4]
103835 **$16.95**

Happy Bird Day!

Hope today tickles you pink!

Hope today tickles you pink!

Tickled Pink [Set of 6]
103205 **$22.95**

100353 Stampin' Around® **Pink Flamingo** **$5.95** (Wheel only. Handle and ink cartridges sold separately. See pages 202–203, 228.)

Happy Birthday Greetings [Set of 1]
100311 **$16.95**

Sweet Treats [Set of 3]
100180 **$17.95**

HUSBAND, WIFE,
...HAPPY LIFE!

100268 Stampin' Around® **Whimsical Blossoms** **$5.95** (Wheel only. Handle and ink cartridges sold separately. See pages 202–203, 228.)

Happy Birthday

Princess

A princess is what you were meant to be, 'cause being sweet comes naturally!

Pretty Princess [Set of 7]
103767 **$22.95**

Class Of

Congratulations

The tassel was worth the hassle!

Class Of 2005

Tassel Time [Set of 9]
101581 **$24.95**

102038 Stampin' Around® **Graduation Day** **$5.95** (Wheel only. Handle and ink cartridges sold separately. See pages 202–203, 228.)

Congratulations
to the
two of you
for choosing
the perfect one.

Wedding
Wishes

Wedding Elegance [Set of 6]
100287 **$19.95**

...From some
of your
closesT
Friends!

ooPS!
iT's a hare
pasT your
birThday!

i know how Much
women your age
enjoy a new
FLoraL Moo-Moo!

hand
sTamped

happy birThday!

i know how M
women your
enjoy a new
FLoraL Moo-M

happy birThday!

we May noT
be TaҀpoLes
anyMore
buT aT LeasT
we haven'T
croakeҀ!

happy birThday!

Birthday Banter [Set of 11]
103814 **$24.95**

102671 Stampin' Around® **Party $5.95** (Wheel only. Handle and ink cartridges sold separately. See pages 202–203, 228.)

Special Day [Set of 1]
104213 **$16.95**

Happily Ever After [Set of 6]
104305 **$16.95**

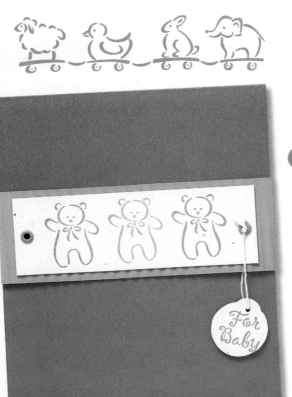

Thank You!

You're Invited!

It's a Shower!

Happy Birthday!

For You

Date:
Time:
Place:

For Baby

DON'T MISS IT! This set has a coordinating Classy Brass® embossing template sold on page 231.

Announcements [Set of 13]
103188 **$26.95**

Date:

Time:

Place:

For:

RSVP:

Welcome, Little One

A new little baby
to cuddle and love,
a bundle from heaven
to think the world of!

A new little baby

Welcome, Little One [Set of 7]
103905 **$19.95**

Congratulations
to you
and your
Somebunny new!

Somebunny New [Set of 4]
103873 **$16.95**

God could not be
everywhere, and
so He created
mothers!

God could not be
everywhere, and
so He created
mothers!

Maternal Instincts [Set of 2]
103959 **$17.95**

DON'T MISS IT! Vellum paper adds a soft touch to your projects. For the white vellum shown on the card above as well as colored vellums in a selection of our 48 colors, see page 205.

Steppin' Style [Set of 13]
101435 **$22.95**

HAPPY BIRTHDAY
To A SPECIAL SOMEONE
WHO'S ALWAYS IN
PERFECT FORM!

FRIEND

FRIENDS
COME IN ALL
SHAPES AND SIZES,
NEED NO
ALTERATIONS,
AND NEVER GO
OUT OF STYLE!

HAPPY BIRTHDAY
To A SPECIAL SOMEONE
WHO'S ALWAYS IN
PERFECT FORM!

I LIKE
YOUR
STYLE!

I Like Your Style [Set of 7]
100144 **$19.95**

104081 Stampin' Around® **Swirl Style** **$5.95** (Wheel only. Handle and ink cartridges sold separately. See pages 202–203, 228.)

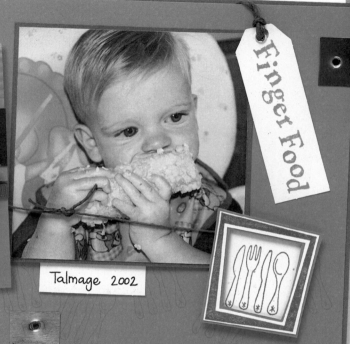

you're invited

Finger Food

Talmage 2002

Definitely Diner [Set of 6]
103879 **$24.95**

Welcome to the neighborhood!

You make me feel right at home!

Happy is the home that shelters a friend.

Thanks for your hospitality!

WE'VE MOVED!

Welcome to the neighborhood!

WE'VE MOVED!

Right at Home [Set of 7]
103765 **$19.95**

HAPPY BIRTHDAY!

HAPPY BIRTHDAY!

IT'S YOUR BIRTHDAY AND I MUST SAY, "YOU LOOK MARVELOUS!"

AND ON MY BIRTHDAY YOU MUST SAY THAT I LOOK MARVELOUS!

REMEMBER WHEN "HIPPIE" MEANT A GROUP OF PEOPLE...

AND NOT THE LOWER HALF OF YOUR BODY?!?

IT'S HARD TO BE NOSTALGIC WHEN YOU CAN'T REMEMBER ANYTHING!

Words by Wanda [Set of 7]
100987 **$19.95**

Friends are the coffee break in the business of life!

Just wanted to Espresso my thanks!

Your friendship Warms my heart.

Happy Birthday to a Regular Joe!

Espress Yourself [Set of 9]
101755 **$24.95**

Visit to Logan

JEN, CODY, AND I HAVE ALL BEEN FRIENDS SINCE WE MET AT USU OUR FRESHMAN YEAR. I STILL GET SO EXCITED EVERY TIME I PLAN A TRIP BACK TO LOGAN TO VISIT THEM.

JANUARY 2004

ooh-la-la!   friends   happy together   hats off!

loves me   Princess   purseonally   relax

yeah, baby   showers of love   sweet   ruff day?

A Little Love [Set of 12]
103739 **$16.95**

IF LIFE'S BORING, MAKE SOMETHING UP!

NEXT YEAR I'LL FORGET MINE!

NEXT YEAR I'LL FORGET MINE!

THAT'S A FIRST!

THANK YOU

TRY THIS! Our 26-gauge Wire Works makes a wonderful complement to our beads (see sample above); use it as a threading tool. In addition, it's thin enough to be shaped easily.

THANK YOU~ I'M SPEECHLESS.

JUST TO SHOW YOU HOW SORRY I AM FOR FORGETTING YOUR BIRTHDAY...

I MISS HEARING FROM YOU...

EVER NOTICE HOW MUCH BETTER RICE CAKES TASTE SMOTHERED IN HOT FUDGE?!?

Wanda's Wit & Wisdom [Set of 7]
104115 **$22.95**

What's for Dinner [Set of 9]
103909 **$26.95**

Cute Critters [Set of 4]
101117 **$11.95**

weLL **i hope you're** Doing we
oPe You're Doing weLL i HoPe You're
oing weLL i HoPe You're Doing weLL
 Doing weLL i HoPe You're Doing weL
You're Doing weLL i HoPe You're Doi
i HoPe You're Doing weLL i HoPe You'
oing weLL i HoPe You're Doing weLL
A're Doing weLL i HoPe You're Doing
oPe You're Doing weLL i HoPe You're
weLL i HoPe You're **doing well**

sTar You are a sTar You are a sTar
you are a sTar You are a sTar
R You are a sTar You are a sTar, Yo
are a sTar You are a sTar You are
sTar You are a sTar You are a sTar
are a sTar You are a sTar You are
You are a sTar You are a sTar You a
AR You are a sTar You are **a star**
 a sTar You are a sTar You are a sT
ou are a sTar, You are a sTar You are

SJ Be HaPPY **don't worry** Be
HaPPY Don'T worrY Be HaPPY Da
worrY Be HaPPY Don'T worrY Be
orrY Be HaPPY Don'T worrY Be H
Be HaPPY Don'T worrY Be HaPPY
Don'T worrY Be HaPPY Don'T wor
PY Don'T worrY Be HaPPY Don'T
HaPPY Don'T worrY Be HaPPY.Do
T worrY **be happy** Don'T wor
PPY Don'T worrY Be HaPPY Don'

BreaTHe **good luck** aND Don'T
aND Don'T ForgeT To BreaTHe goo
ucK aND Don'T ForgeT To BreaTH
gooD LucK aND Don'T ForgeT To B
THe gooD LucK aND Don'T ForgeT
cK aND Don'T ForgeT To BreaTH.
Don'T ForgeT To BreaTHe go
ForgeT To BreaT
gooD LucK **and** go
rjeT **to brea**

 Heads Up [Set of 8]
103899 **$26.95**

Just a Note

Jazzed Up [Set of 6]
104137 **$17.95**

104158 Stampin' Around® **Jazz** **$5.95** (Wheel only. Handle and ink cartridges sold separately. See pages 202–203, 228.)

I never met a chocolate I didn't like.

Making the world sweeter, one chocolate at a time.

The best things in life are chocolate!

The best things

Oh So Sweet [Set of 8]
103744 **$19.95**

You warm my heart

You Warm My Heart [Set of 8]
100194 **$19.95**

You warm my heart

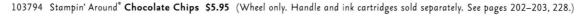

103794 Stampin' Around® **Chocolate Chips** **$5.95** (Wheel only. Handle and ink cartridges sold separately. See pages 202–203, 228.)

100356 Stampin' Around® **Totally Teacups** **$5.95** (Wheel only. Handle and ink cartridges sold separately. See pages 202–203, 228.)

Thank You

DON'T MISS IT! This set is also sold as part of a kit on page 24.

All Natural [Set of 6]
104473 **$16.95**

STAMPIN' STEP STAMPIN'

All the Best

LOVE

Thanks

Thank You

Thanks

All the Best

emma Lyn is seemingly sweet beyond words. i am very grateful to have her as my daughter and friend. we took this photo one spring afternoon just after a party we attended celebrating her grandparents 50th anniversary. she looked so sweet and innocent in her simple white dress and bare feet. emma Lyn is an endearing part of my life.

april 2003

STAMPIN' STEP STAMPIN'

All the Best [Set of 7]
103895 **$19.95**

DON'T MISS IT! This set is also sold as part of a kit on page 25.

I Am a Child of God

Return with Honor

Kindness Begins
With Me

Jesus is the Reason
for the Season

Love is Spoken Here

Count Your Blessings

I Am a Child of God

Count Your Blessings

Choose The Right

Make a joyful noise
unto the Lord

All God's Children [Set of 8]
100283 **$19.95**

THIS
LITTLE
LIGHT
OF
MINE—

I'M
GONNA
LET
IT
SHINE!

WITH
GOD,
ALL
THINGS
ARE
POSSIBLE.

LITTLE
LAMBS,
SO
WHITE
AND
FAIR,
ARE
THE
SHEPHERD'S
CONSTANT
CARE.

THIS
LITTLE
LIGHT
OF
MINE—
I'M
GONNA
LET
IT
SHINE!

WHAT

WOULD

JESUS

DO?

Little Inspirations [Set of 4]
101595 **$19.95**

Friends like you keep me afloat.

Love is found where you least expect it.

Friends are flowers that never fade.

A real friend is one who drops in when the rest of the world drops out.

Friends like you keep me afloat.

Favorite Friends [Set of 7]
103827 **$19.95**

ooh ~la~ la!

1st woof

merci!

merci! merci! merci! merci! merci!

Paris in the Spring [Set of 7]
103933 **$19.95**

104044 Stampin' Around® **Springtime** **$5.95** (Wheel only. Handle and ink cartridges sold separately. See pages 202–203, 228.)

sentiments

Remember... "stressed" spelled backwards is "desserts!"

Hang in there!

never forget...
you're never forgotten!

I'm O.K.... really I am

Hang in There [Set of 6]
103052 **$24.95**

Oh, Hi!

Oh, Please!

Oh, Yes!

Oh, My!

Charming Children [Set of 4]
104235 **$14.95**

Bottles and booties,
bibs and more,
a new little
someone
to love and adore!

ISN'T SHE adorable?

first pictures!

it is hard to describe our feelings. you are so beautiful, so tiny, and so sweet! we can hardly believe you are ours. what a blessing you are!
Jamie Lynn Stevens 2/10/03

Bottles and booties,
bibs and more,
a new little
someone
to love and adore!

welcome, little one

DON'T MISS IT! This set has coordinating boy and girl Simply Scrappin® kits sold on page 212.

A New Little Someone [Set of 7]
103635 **$19.95**

carrots peas plums

103749 Stampin' Around® Jumbo **Wash Day $7.95** (Wheel only. Handle and ink cartridges sold separately. See pages 202–203, 228.)

ever since jamison Learned To say "Train", ThaT's all we ever hear abouT. he Loves anyThing ThaT has To do wiTh Trains; movies, books, and Toys. Today i Told him we were going on a real Train. he wouldn'T sTop asking when we were going.

march 3, 2003

Little Engine [Set of 6]
104095 **$17.95**

he's here

Baby Firsts [Set of 8]
102341 **$19.95**

101420 Stampin' Around® **Baby Time** **$5.95** (Wheel only. Handle and ink cartridges sold separately. See pages 202–203, 228.)

Jonah

b a b y

Baby Benjamin

TIME GOES BY SO QUICKLY.
IT FEELS LIKE JUST YESTERDAY
WE WERE BRINGING BENJAMIN
HOME FROM THE HOSPITAL.
THESE PAST TWO MONTHS
HAVE GONE BY SO FAST.
IT IS EXCITING TO SEE BENJAMIN
GROW AND LEARN NEW THINGS.
THIS MONTH HE HAS LEARNED
TO LAUGH AND SMILE.
HIS LAUGH IS A SWEET GIGGLE
AND HIS SMILE BRINGS SO MUCH
JOY INTO OUR LIVES.

MAY 2001

i'm here

abcdefgh
ijklmnop
qrstuvw
xyzabcd
efghijkl
mnopqrs
tuvwxyz

TRY THIS! The letters in this alphabet can be punched out with the 1/4-inch Circle punch (page 222).

I'm Here* [Set of 6]
104215 **$24.95**

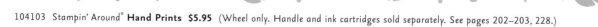

104103 Stampin' Around® **Hand Prints** **$5.95** (Wheel only. Handle and ink cartridges sold separately. See pages 202–203, 228.)

100593 Stampin' Around® **Sweet Feet** **$5.95** (Wheel only. Handle and ink cartridges sold separately. See pages 202–203, 228.)

friends

Definitely Decorative® **Crayon Kids** [Set of 10]
101135 **$32.95**

DON'T MISS IT! The Crayon Kids and Crayon Fun sets
coordinate with the Crayon Fun Alphabet on page 196.

Definitely Decorative® **Crayon Fun** [Set of 6]
100289 **$19.95**

100269 Stampin' Around® **Crayon ABCs $5.95** (Wheel only. Handle and ink cartridges sold separately. See pages 202–203, 228.)

GOOD IDEA!

KEEP UP THE GOOD WORK!

DINOMITE!

A

Toadally Awesome!

YOU DID IT!

Teacher Time [Set of 6]
102088 **$16.95**

me & my **SISTER**

Jane and rachel are not only sisters but also best friends. They love being with each other each and every waking moment of the day. I cherish the times that I see them laughing together, playing together and even quarreling with each other. each moment they share they seem to find more reasons to love each other not only as sisters but as friends.

June 2003

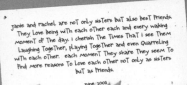

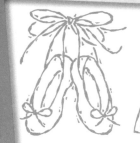

FRIEND

Buttons, Bows & Twinkletoes [Set of 13]
103626 **$24.95**

DON'T MISS IT! This set has a coordinating Simply Scrappin® kit sold on page 213.

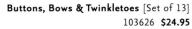

Toy Box [Set of 13]
102071 **$24.95**

DON'T MISS IT! This set has a coordinating Simply Scrappin'® kit sold on page 214.

Dino-Mite [Set of 6]
100020 **$19.95**

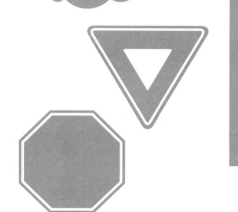

going places

Grandpa W. saw this fire truck and couldn't resist buying it for Cameron. It will be a while before Cameron grows into it, but it was fun to see my Dad so into his grandson.

June 2003

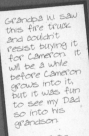

© 2004 STAMPIN' UP!

Definitely Decorative® **Road Trip** [Set of 6]
104211 **$21.95**

Little Trucks [Set of 6]
102936 **$19.95**

thanks

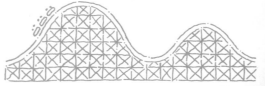

Time for fun

We took Shannon to the State Fair for her birthday. I think she liked riding on the carousel best! She rode it ten times!

June 12, 2003

Time for fun!

Time for Fun [Set of 7]
103618 **$19.95**

DON'T MISS IT! This set has a coordinating Simply Scrappin® kit sold on page 213.

FAMILY TRIP

growing up

WELCOME TO KENNECOTT

We spent a few hours touring the copper mines at Kennecott before we continued on to visit Grandma Lee.
8·27·03

WELCOME TO

ARE WE THERE YET?

...OR BUST!

MAP

i miss you

Travel Time [Set of 9]
102258 **$28.95**

DON'T MISS IT! This set has a coordinating Simply Scrappin® kit sold on page 215.

103748 Stampin' Around® Jumbo **Carnival Fun** **$7.95** (Wheel only. Handle and ink cartridges sold separately. See pages 202–203, 228.)

Kids at Play [Set of 9]
101043 **$24.95**

$2.00 from the sale of each **Kid Cards** set supports Ronald McDonald House Charities!

Stampin' Up! is a national sponsor of Ronald McDonald House Charities (RMHC)®—and we're pleased to offer this exclusive stamp set to all of our customers! We'll donate $2 from the sale of each **Kid Cards** set to RMHC, an organization committed to improving the lives of children and their families throughout the world. When you buy the set, you make a difference in the lives of children and families served by RMHC.

HAPPY BIRTHDAY!

HAPPY HOLIDAYS!

THANK YOU

GOOD FOR YOU!

Kid Cards [Set of 4]
103943 **$14.95**

whatever!

ITS YOUR DAY!

Girlfriends

Girlfriends [Set of 8]
101573 **$21.95**

In your dreams!

DIARY

Girl talk

KAYCE AND BRITTNEY WOULD RATHER SPEND TIME WITH GRAMMA M. THAN WITH ANYONE ELSE ON EARTH! IT DOESN'T MATTER IF THEY'RE SHOPPING, HAVING LUNCH, OR JUST HANGIN' OUT. IT'S ALWAYS A PARTY. I'M SO GLAD WE LIVE CLOSE ENOUGH TO MOM THAT MY GIRLS CAN HAVE THIS KIND OF RELATIONSHIP WITH HER. I KNOW THEY'LL ALWAYS BE CLOSE TO HER AND I COULDN'T ASK FOR A BETTER ROLE MODEL FOR THEM. OCT 2002

Girlfriends Accessories [Set of 8]
103226 **$16.95**

a little
something
just
for you

friends
are like
pockets...
you can
never have
too many!

Pocket Fun [Set of 7]
100162 **$19.95**

TRY THIS! Crumpled paper adds dimension and interest to your stamping projects. Start at one edge and bend a portion back and forth between your fingers. Work your way across the sheet until the surface is completely crumpled.

friends
are like
pockets...
you can
never have
too many!

Definitely Decorative® **Tea Time** [Set of 6]
100279 **$28.95**

you make me smile

All Wrapped Up [Set of 7]
104036 **$19.95**

celebrate

summer

All Wrapped Up Accessories [Set of 6]
104038 **$9.95**

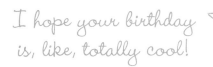

I hope your birthday is, like, totally cool!

I'd rather be shopping!

I'd rather be shopping!

Totally Cool [Set of 7]
104073 **$19.95**

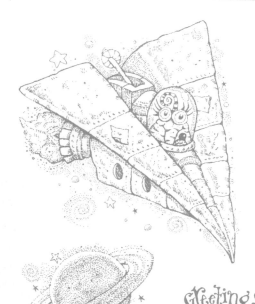

To the Finish [Set of 6]
100184 **$22.95**

TRY THIS! Smashed brads add an interesting element. Avoid creating dents or creases in your card stock by hammering the brads on scratch paper first, then adding them to your project.

Greetings, Earthlings

Hope your day is out of this World!

Out of This World [Set of 7]
103833 **$19.95**

PLAY ✕ BALL

One of Braxton's favorite things to do in the summer is to go to the park and play baseball with dad. Dad helps Braxton with his swing. This time I decided to tag along and take some pictures.   June 2004

to: Ryan
from: Ben

Sporting Goods [Set of 14]
104120 **$28.95**

104159 Stampin' Around® Jumbo **Sports Fans** **$7.95** (Wheel only. Handle and ink cartridges sold separately. See pages 202–203, 228.)

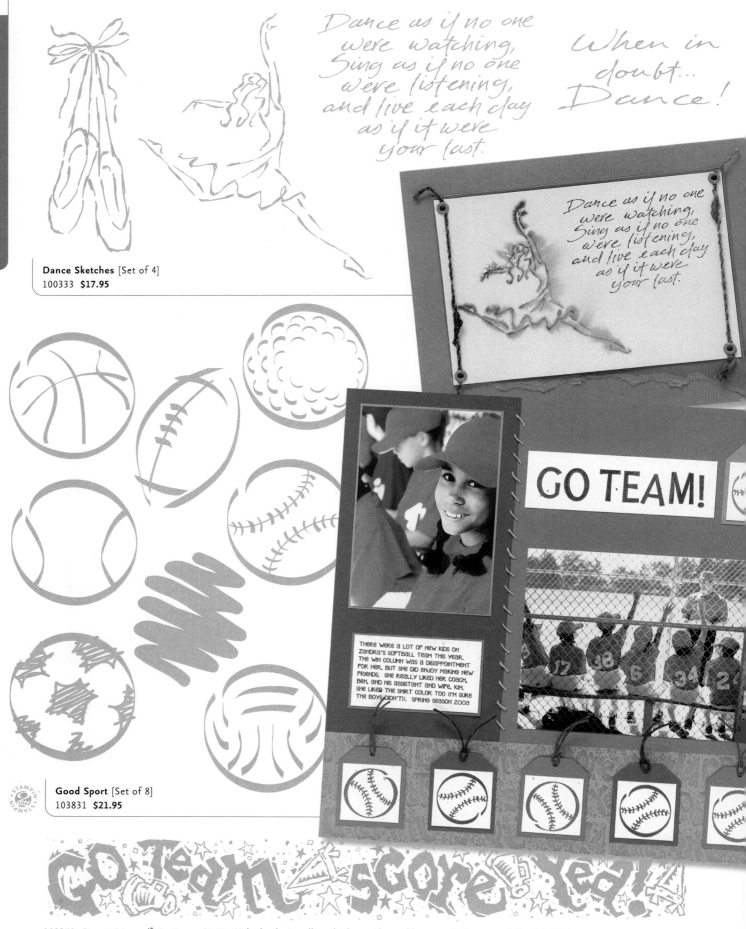

Dance Sketches [Set of 4]
100333 **$17.95**

Dance as if no one were watching, Sing as if no one were listening, and live each day as if it were your last.

When in doubt... Dance!

Good Sport [Set of 8]
103831 **$21.95**

GO TEAM!

There were a lot of new kids on Zandra's softball team this year. The win column was a disappointment for her, but she did enjoy making new friends. She really liked her coach, Ben, and his assistant and wife, Kim. She liked the shirt color too (I'm sure the boys didn't). Spring Season 2003

102340 Stampin' Around® **Go Team** **$5.95** (Wheel only. Handle and ink cartridges sold separately. See pages 202–203, 228.)

How cute is that **giggle**?

I can almost hear your giggle when I look at these pictures. Everytime you giggle, we giggle, which makes you giggle and so on and so on... Isabelle at five months.

Definitely Decorative® **Gladsome Garden** [Set of 6]
104113 **$22.95**

104067 Stampin' Around® Jumbo **Posies & Polka Dots** **$7.95** (Wheel only. Handle and ink cartridges sold separately. See pages 202–203, 228.)

Mojan, Mia, and Daddy at HoJLe Zoo's aviary.
June 2004

for the BiRDS

Definitely Decorative® **Springtime Fun** [Set of 12]
101488 **$34.95**

it may not be yellowstone, but it's sure a lot less work for me to let the kids sleep out in the backyard. this summer jake was finally old enough to join Lyndsey and Braden for their traditional Fourth of July campout, but once it got dark, he was all for coming in the house to his own bed. i'm glad he's not too grown up yet.

JULY 4, 2004

for my sweet daughter

DON'T MISS IT! This set coordinates with the Sweet & Sassy Designer Series paper and vellum sold on page 209. If you like this set, see the coordinating stamping kit sold on page 27.

Buds & Blossoms [Set of 7]
103633 **$19.95**

104101 Stampin' Around® **Delicate Design** **$5.95** (Wheel only. Handle and ink cartridges sold separately. See pages 202–203, 228.)

103752 Stampin' Around® Jumbo **Bold Blooms** **$7.95** (Wheel only. Handle and ink cartridges sold separately. See pages 202–203, 228.)

Love without End [Set of 9]
100152 **$24.95**

DON'T MISS IT! This set has a coordinating Classy Brass® embossing template sold on page 231, as well as coordinating Alphadots and Alphadot Numbers sets on page 196.

Watercolor Garden II [Set of 9]
102724 **$28.95**

Definitely Decorative® Bloomin' Wonderful [Set of 9]
104165 **$28.95**

DON'T MISS IT! This set has a coordinating Classy Brass®
embossing template sold on page 231.

104098 Stampin' Around® **Whirly-Twirly** **$5.95** (Wheel only. Handle and ink cartridges sold separately. See pages 202–203, 228.)

summer garden party

i really like This picture of grace and Leon helping out aT our summer parTy. They have become greaT Friends. The Food was greaT This year and The weaTher cooperaTed Too. The whole evenT wenT parTicularly well, and i FelT really greaT aT The end of The nighT.   also, ThankFul For good Friends. July 2003

Definitely Decorative® **Daisy** [Set of 13]
101486 **$29.95**

DON'T MISS IT! This set has a coordinating Classy Brass® embossing template sold on page 231.

to my mom

Watercolor Minis [Set of 12]
104468 **$17.95**

may
hope
fill
your
heart

Exotic Blooms [Set of 6]
103911 **$17.95**

scatter seeds
of kindness

scatter seeds
of kindness

scatter seeds
of kindness

Seeds of Kindness [Set of 6]
100295 **$19.95**

100270 Stampin' Around® **Dandelions** **$5.95** (Wheel only. Handle and ink cartridges sold separately. See pages 202–203, 228.)

Stipple Rose [Set of 1]
101960 **$12.95**

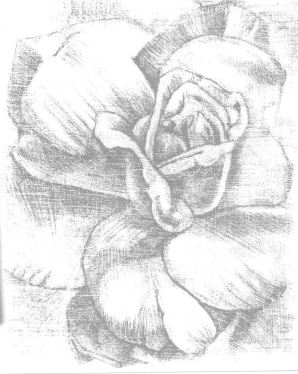

Elegant Rose [Set of 1]
100255 **$12.95**

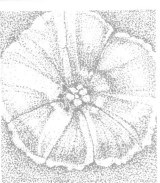

Perfect Petals [Set of 4]
100327 **$14.95**

Memory is the power to gather roses in winter.

The fragrance lingers in the hand that gives the rose.

Definitely Decorative® Roses in Winter [Set of 9]
100386 **$28.95**

Love is the sunshine that warms each soul to blossom.

Beautiful wishes for a beautiful day.

Beautiful wishes for a beautiful day.

Heaven Scent [Set of 6]
104219 **$19.95**

Terrific Tulips [Set of 9]
102783 **$24.95**

Early Spring [Set of 3]
100384 **$22.95**

104155 Stampin' Around® Jumbo **Lilies** **$7.95** (Wheel only. Handle and ink cartridges sold separately. See pages 202–203, 228.)

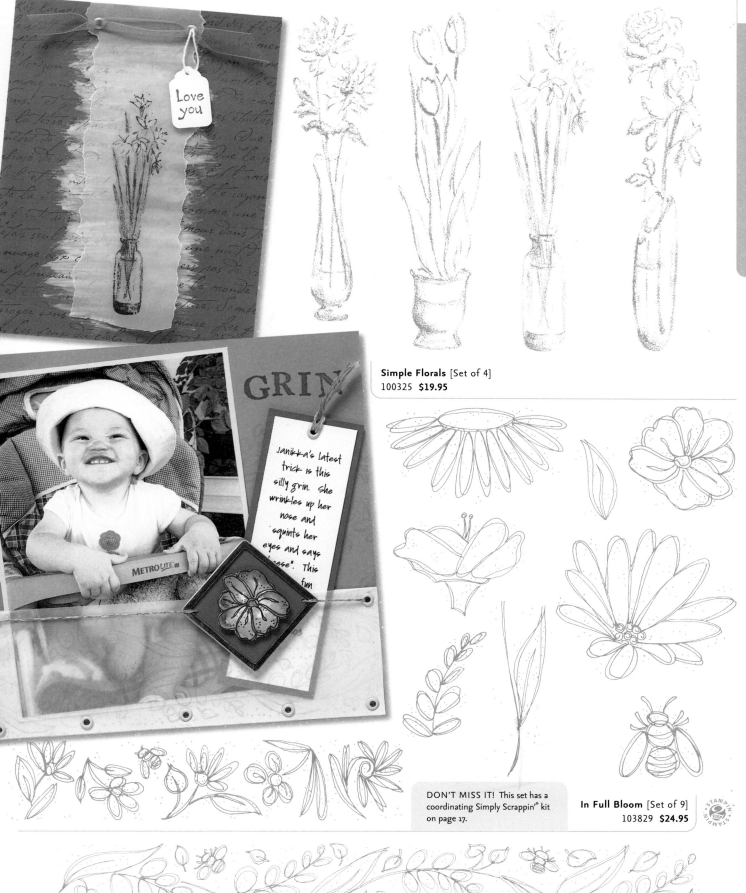

Simple Florals [Set of 4]
100325 **$19.95**

DON'T MISS IT! This set has a
coordinating Simply Scrappin® kit
on page 17.

In Full Bloom [Set of 9]
103829 **$24.95**

104070 Stampin' Around® **Bloomin'** **$5.95** (Wheel only. Handle and ink cartridges sold separately. See pages 202–203, 228.)

flowers

Delightful Doodles [Set of 4]
100703 **$11.95**

DON'T MISS IT! This set has a coordinating Classy Brass® embossing template sold on page 231.

DON'T MISS IT! This set has a coordinating Classy Brass® embossing template sold on page 231.

Fresh Flowers [Set of 9]
102751 **$24.95**

103112 Stampin' Around® **Blossoms & Bugs** **$5.95** (Wheel only. Handle and ink cartridges sold separately. See pages 202–203, 228.)

© 1990–2004 Stampin' Up!

happy spring

because I care!

TRY THIS! Practice the design you want on poster board before stamping a wall.

Definitely Decorative® **Build a Blossom** [Set of 4]
103538 **$16.95**

102776 Stampin' Around® **Tulip** **$5.95** (Wheel only. Handle and ink cartridges sold separately. See pages 202–203, 228.)

Live well,
laugh often,
love much.

Spring Garden [Set of 9]
101857 **$24.95**

just a note

Thanks for
touching my life
with your special
friendship!

Thanks for
touching my life
with your special
friendship!

Watercolor Garden [Set of 13]
101352 **$26.95**

Close to Nature [Set of 4]
104475 **$11.95**

issus poeticus, Caladium comes
la, Begonia pearcei, Zinnia
ia maculata, Crocus indiflor
cardinalis, Hyacinthus, Tuli
lium concolor, Wistaria chine
ia comta superba, Orchis mac
siflora caerulea, Rosa noisetti
nia thunbergia, Hydrangea hor,

Celebrate

To Someone Special

3

a.

To Someone Special

12

Botanicals [Set of 9]
101642 **$28.95**

Sun-Ripened II [Set of 3]
100887 **$17.95**

TRY THIS! Tearing paper gives it
an aged look. Take it a step further
by curling the torn edges.

for you

Wonderful Wings [Set of 4]
100571 **$29.95**

Thanks

Autumn [Set of 5]
102674 **$21.95**

thanks for your kindness

Lovely As a Tree [Set of 6]
101223 **$24.95**

OUTDOORS

Zach and Justin were reluctant travelers as we made our way to our family reunion. They weren't sure what a weekend without television or video games would be like. We assured them that they would not have time to be bored! Turns out, they had the best time! They found new friends in distant relatives, and they learned about archery, rode horses, and played games. As we drove home, Zach said, "Now we know what it must have been like a way long time ago when you and Dad were kids!"

SUMMER 2003

For you

Definitely Decorative® Pines [Set of 6]
100863 **$24.95**

101525 Stampin' Around® **Great Outdoors** $5.95 (Wheel only. Handle and ink cartridges sold separately. See pages 202–203, 228.)

In The Moment

It's not often that Todd and I get the same weekend off of work - it seemed a perfect opportunity to get away with the children. We decided on a day-long hike in Southern Utah. The weather was great, and the children loved our hike. McKenna collected rocks, Dalton wanted to collect a few beetles, but I just couldn't stand the thought of bringing bugs back to Salt Lake with us. Judging by her happy smile and the occasional squeal, Malee thought it was pretty fun to ride on Daddy's back. We were all in the moment, taking it all in, and enjoying being together.

Spring 2003

for my father

Roughing It [Set of 17]
101395 **$29.95**

Life is a picnic, eat hearty!

Ladybug Picnic [Set of 5]
103777 **$22.95**

Life is a picnic, eat hearty!

many thanks

Bunch o' Bugs [Set of 6]
101969 **$16.95**

101391 Stampin' Around® **Dragonfly** **$5.95** (Wheel only. Handle and ink cartridges sold separately. See pages 202–203, 228.)

summer

6.6.03

Chantal was so excited about her new bike! We took her to the neighborhood park and watched her excitement as she learned to ride. She got the hang of it quickly, and now she rides her bike almost every day.

smile smile smile smile smile smile sm

Definitely Decorative® **Bold Butterfly** [Set of 6]
103804 **$28.95**

104156 Stampin' Around® Jumbo **Flitting By $7.95** (Wheel only. Handle and ink cartridges sold separately. See pages 202–203, 228.)

Cold-Weather Friends [Set of 6]
100124 **$18.95**

many
thanks

I think of you

Yukon [Set of 6]
103001 **$21.95**

© 2002 STAMPIN' UP!

© 2002 STAMPIN' UP!

Noble Deer [Set of 4]
103825 **$17.95**

There's a longstanding tradition in the Hollowell family that the person who catches the smallest fish tells the "biggest fish" story—and it was Jake's turn this time: "I was sitting there minding my own business, enjoying the quiet morning, when I feel a big tug on my line. There in the middle of the river was the biggest trout I'd ever seen! He must have been 3 feet long and at least 10 pounds! Just like dad taught me, i alternated between feeding him some line and reeling him in, until i could see the whites of his eyes, and boy oh boy was he a big ol' sucker—just like you are if you believe this story!"

cripple creek
october 2003

Angler [Set of 4]
103963 **$17.95**

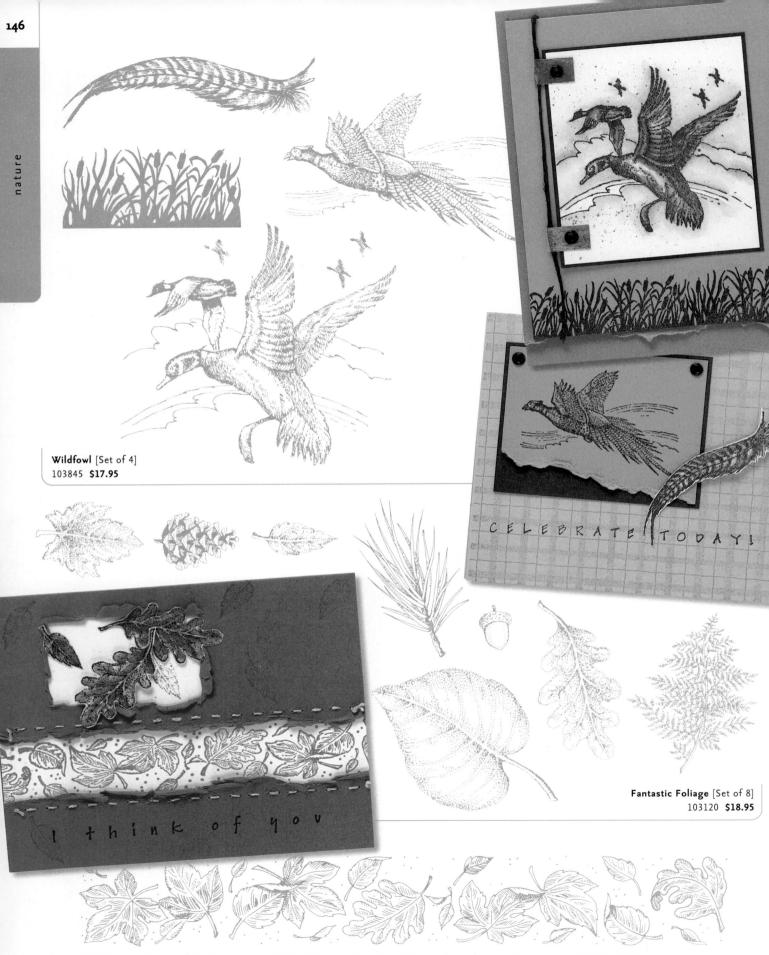

Wildfowl [Set of 4]
103845 **$17.95**

CELEBRATE TODAY!

I think of you

Fantastic Foliage [Set of 8]
103120 **$18.95**

101909 Stampin' Around® **Swirling Leaves** **$5.95** (Wheel only. Handle and ink cartridges sold separately. See pages 202–203, 228.)

Discovery

KATE AND SAM

SUMMER 2003

Have A Great Day!

Aquaria [Set of 7]
103823 **$19.95**

Stipple Shells [Set of 6]
101580 **$14.95**

thank you

103094 Stampin' Around® **By the Sea** **$5.95** (Wheel only. Handle and ink cartridges sold separately. See pages 202–203, 228.)

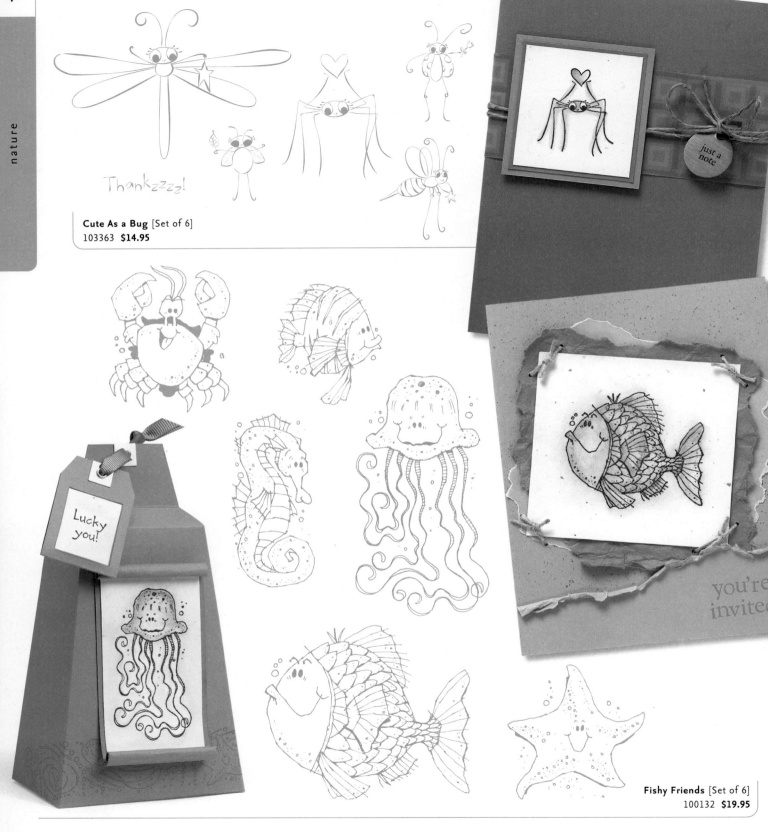

Cute As a Bug [Set of 6]
103363 **$14.95**

just a note

Lucky you!

you're invited

Fishy Friends [Set of 6]
100132 **$19.95**

Thankzzzz!

104065 Stampin' Around® **Fishy** **$5.95** (Wheel only. Handle and ink cartridges sold separately. See pages 202–203, 228.)

Fintastic [Set of 4]
103812 **$18.95**

little
BUGS

our family just loves
to spend time in the outdoors.
These photos were taken when
we were hiking up little
cottonwood canyon this past
summer. benjamin and andrew
just loved inspecting all the
insects they spotted along the
trail. the hike took us twice
as long, but it was worth
taking the time to explore
nature and to see the children
so excited about the outdoors.

summer 2003

Bug Builders [Set of 11]
102739 **$24.95**

103059 Stampin' Around® **Bitty Bugs $5.95** (Wheel only. Handle and ink cartridges sold separately. See pages 202–203, 228.)

nature

thanks friend

thanks friend

On the Farm [Set of 7]
102203 **$19.95**

When we go to Grandma and Grandpa Lee's farm, Alexa loves to pet the horses and Jane loves to see the cows.

Autumn 2003

On the Farm

104066 Stampin' Around® Jumbo **Farmyard** **$7.95** (Wheel only. Handle and ink cartridges sold separately. See pages 202–203, 228.)

Happiness
is a warm puppy
charles schulz

Puppy Love [Set of 4]
103841 **$17.95**

The wind of heaven
is that which
blows between a
horse's ears.

Bareback [Set of 4]
103907 **$18.95**

In all things of nature, there is something of the marvelous.
—Aristotle

Something Marvelous [Set of 4]
103737 **$17.95**

Camden at the city zoo June 2002

In the Wild [Set of 6]
100321 **$19.95**

DON'T MISS IT! The In the Wild set coordinates with the On Safari background stamp on page 180.

104062 Stampin' Around® **Heart of Africa** **$5.95** (Wheel only. Handle and ink cartridges sold separately. See pages 202–203, 228.)

bow wow · ruff · arff

XOXO

I'm sorry

Canine ~~~ [Set of 7]
100345

*it's ~~ough
b~ng
pur~fect*

Purrfect [Set ~
100170 **$16.9~**

it's purrfect

100359 S~ ~ Around® **Feline Friends** **$5.95** (Wheel only. Handle and ink cartridges sold separately. See pages 202–203, 228.)

bow wow

ar~f

ruff ruff.

10036~ ~mpin' Around® **Playful Pups** **$5.95** (Wheel only. Handle and ink cartridges sold separately. See pages 202–203, 228.)

Born to Ride [Set of 6]
100096 **$21.95**

Fire Brigade [Set of 4]
104018 **$17.95**

104100 Stampin' Around® **Making Tracks** **$5.95**
(Wheel only. Handle and ink cartridges sold separately. See pages 202–203, 228.)

I think of you

FATHER

Classic Convertibles [Set of 3]
100022 **$17.95**

Maine

Oregon

North Scotia

North Carolina

Coast to Coast [Set of 4]
103175 **$27.95**

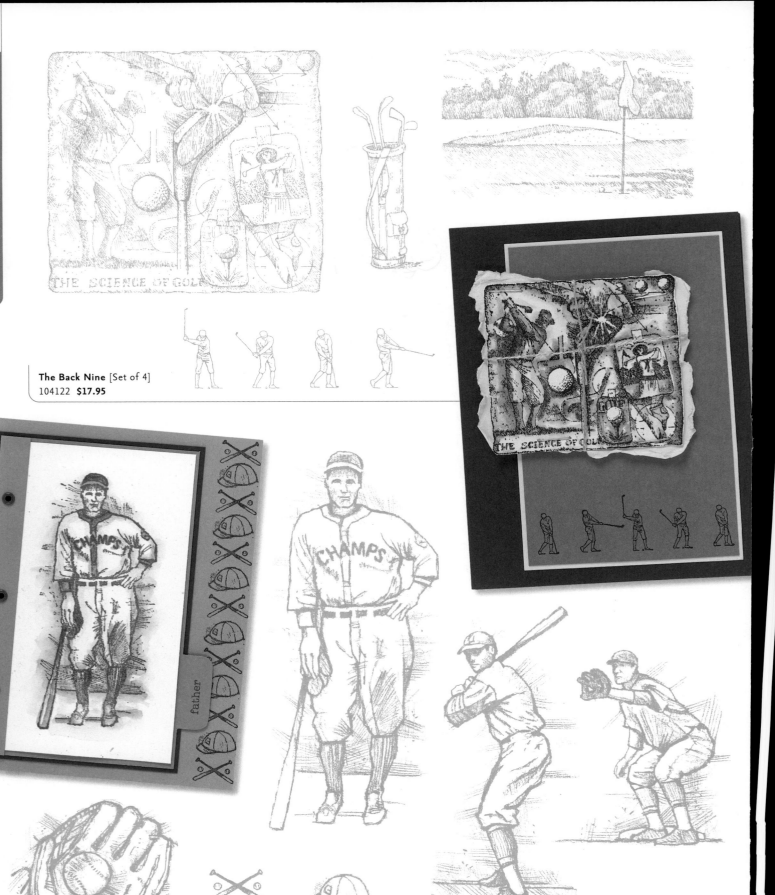

The Back Nine [Set of 4]
104122 **$17.95**

Take Me Out to the Ball Game [Set of 6]
100114 **$22.95**

You Touch My Life

Set Sail [Set of 4]
103837 **$17.95**

In the Sky [Set of 4]
102344 **$11.95**

Netherlands [Set of 4]
103897 **$16.95**

vintage

What each of us becomes
is fashioned from
the Stardust of
our dreams

Stardust [Set of 4]
103818 **$18.95**

Savannah 2003

HAWAII

Beautiful Batik [Set of 9]
102628 **$24.95**

101282 Stampin' Around® **Batik** **$5.95** (Wheel only. Handle and ink cartridges sold separately. See pages 202–203, 228.)

the cow jumped over the moon...

Rub-a-dub-dub, three men in a tub...

Humpty-Dumpty sat on a wall...

Mary had a little lamb...

Rhyme Time [Set of 4]
104124 **$27.95**

Star-Spangled Banner [Set of 4]
103839 **$14.95**

Country Fresh [Set of 4]
100331 **$14.95**

Etruscan [Set of 14]
100943 **$28.95**

100355 Stampin' Around® **Etruscan Vine** **$5.95** (Wheel only. Handle and ink cartridges sold separately. See pages 202–203, 228.)

FRESH

FRAGILE

thank you
very much

Farm Fresh [Set of 6]
103196 **$19.95**

Friendship is a journey of time, love, and memories.

Friendship's Journey [Set of 4]
100018 **$16.95**

Travels Abroad [Set of 6]
100186 **$21.95**

Parisian Plaza [Set of 6]
100098 **$21.95**

Nostalgia [Set of 4]
104091 **$17.95**

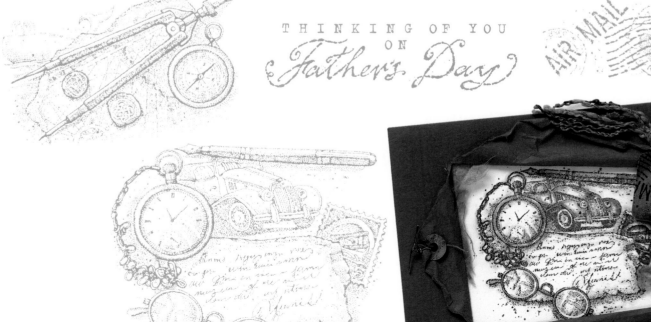

Thinking of Father [Set of 4]
103931 **$17.95**

Calming Garden [Set of 5]
103881 **$22.95**

TRY THIS! Repeated layers of heat embossing are the secret to the accent on the card at right. After embossing several layers, stamp the image while the embossing is still hot.

Elegant Ornaments [Set of 4]
100277 **$14.95**

智 愛 和 安

wisdom   *love*   *harmony*   *tranquility*

Kanji [Set of 4]
102081 **$11.95**

Oriental Brushstrokes [Set of 4]
104089 **$17.95**

Art of the Orient [Set of 4]
100339 **$11.95**

Definitely Decorative® **Toile Blossoms** [Set of 7]
100418 **$32.95**

Mostly Flowers [Set of 4]
104480 **$11.95**

thank you

Gentler Times [Set of 7]
103746 **$22.95**

Appreciation

is the

memory

of the heart.

Memory of the Heart [Set of 6]
104479 **$16.95**

SisTErs

© 1990–2004 STAMPIN' UP!

Flora & Fauna [Set of 7]
104142 **$28.95**

¡ Love you more!

Loving Theodore

July 2003

happy
small
lovable

Swirl Frame Fun [Set of 7]
101792 **$28.95**

100662 Stampin' Around® **Swirl Fun** **$5.95** (Wheel only. Handle and ink cartridges sold separately. See pages 202–203, 228.)

HAPPY
*Mother's
Day*

Alice G. Long, Thomas Jr., Mary Gard, and Thomas Henry Long 1927

Our Family

*Katrina,
Jay's
and Grace
2004*

*Sweet
baby
Grace
7 months*

Frame & Flourishes [Set of 7]
101931 **$28.95**

DON'T MISS IT! The samples on this page use
Tudor Designer Series paper sold on page 208.

Woodland Frame [Set of 7]
104161 **$28.95**

TRY THIS! In addition to framing photos, the frames in our frame sets can be used to create card fronts and borders.

Shining Star [Set of 7]
103629 **$28.95**

Letter Perfect Backgrounds [Set of 4]
104241 **$11.95**

Fine Frames [Set of 4]
103810 **$14.95**

Borders Mini [Set of 4]
102019 **$11.95**

DON'T MISS IT! The small frame sets on these two pages are perfect for framing images and greetings from the Year-Round Fun II, Everyday Flexible Phrases, and Tiny Talk sets as well as letters in our alphabet sets.

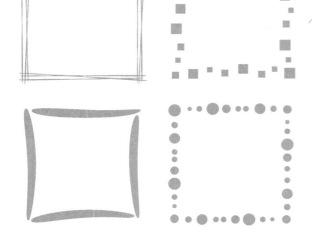

Around & About [Set of 4]
104474 **$11.95**

congratulations!

Itty Bitty Backgrounds [Set of 4]
101893 **$11.95**

YOU'RE MY HERO!

Stars & Swirls [Set of 4]
100851 **$11.95**

Happy Happy Birthday

Background Basics [Set of 4]
100970 **$11.95**

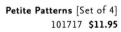

Beyond the Basics [Set of 4]
102475 **$11.95**

Petite Patterns [Set of 4]
101717 **$11.95**

Fresh Fillers [Set of 4]
104476 **$11.95**

DON'T MISS IT! This set has a coordinating Classy Brass® embossing template sold on page 231.

Border Builders [Set of 9]
102573 **$21.95**

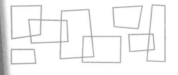

Smorgasborders [Set of 9]
103798 **$16.95**

8·3·03

HAPPY Thanksgiving

Itty Bitty Borders [Set of 4]
100554 **$11.95**

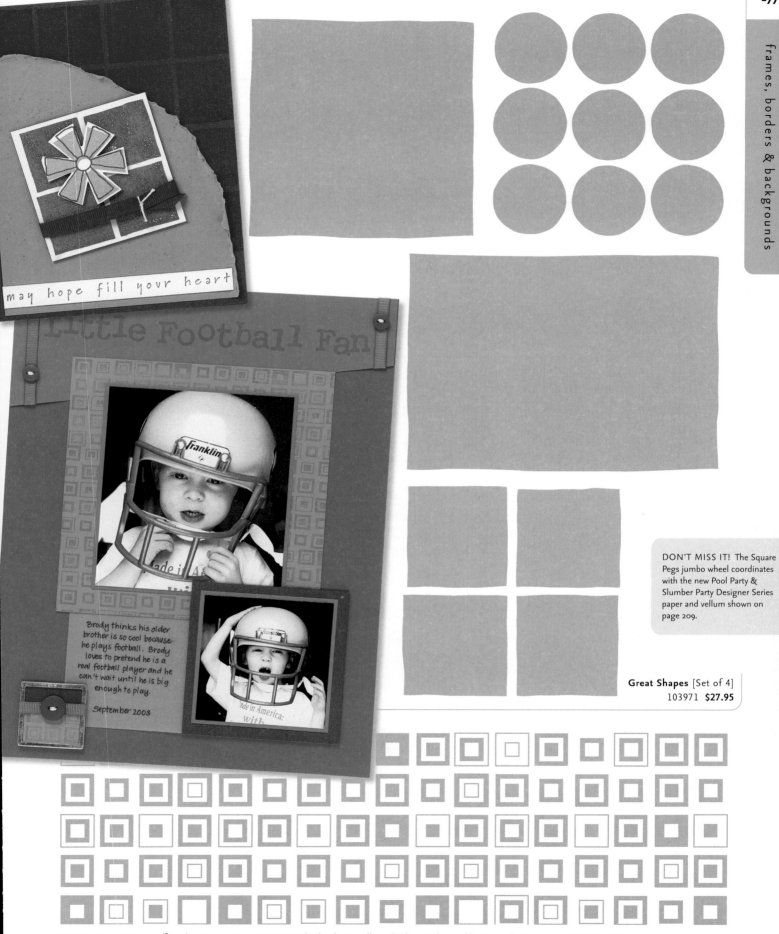

may hope fill your heart

Little Football Fan

Brody thinks his older brother is so cool because he plays football. Brody loves to pretend he is a real football player and he can't wait until he is big enough to play.

September 2003

DON'T MISS IT! The Square Pegs jumbo wheel coordinates with the new Pool Party & Slumber Party Designer Series paper and vellum shown on page 209.

Great Shapes [Set of 4]
103971 **$27.95**

104160 Stampin' Around® Jumbo **Square Pegs** **$7.95** (Wheel only. Handle and ink cartridges sold separately. See pages 202–203, 228.)

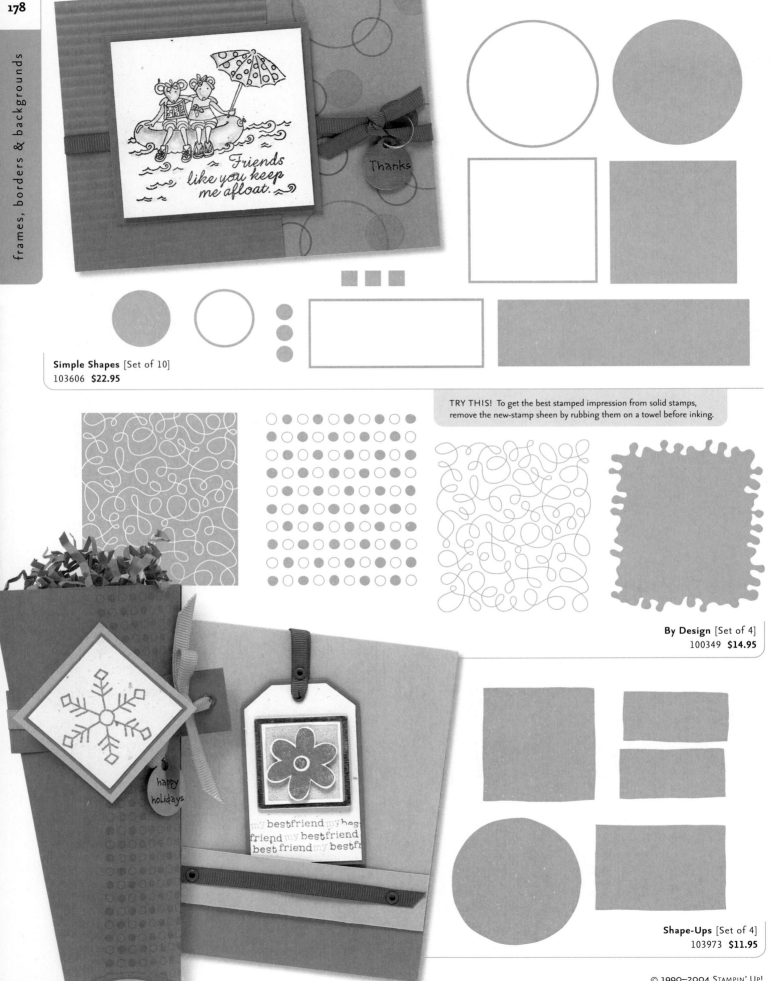

Simple Shapes [Set of 10]
103606 **$22.95**

TRY THIS! To get the best stamped impression from solid stamps, remove the new-stamp sheen by rubbing them on a towel before inking.

By Design [Set of 4]
100349 **$14.95**

Shape-Ups [Set of 4]
103973 **$11.95**

Paisley Print [Set of 1]
104030 **$16.95**

Approximate dimensions for all background stamps on pages 179–181 are 4-1/2 x 5-3/4 (large enough to cover a standard-sized card). With the exception of the full stamp shown at left, all background stamps show a portion of the pattern at actual size.

love ('ləv) n. 1. A de
feeling of affection and
uch as that arising fr
attractive qualities,.
oneness. / harmony ('hä
feeling; accord: live
combination of elements
3. The combination of si
a chord. / peace (pēs) n
or quiet. 2. The absence
reedom from quarrels a
(frend) n. 1. One who

By Definition [Set of 1]
100307 **$16.95**

Swirls & Blossoms [Set of 1]
100182 **$16.95**

Dots & Checks [Set of 1]
103955 **$16.95**

Simple Stripes [Set of 1]
103534 **$16.95**

French Script [Set of 1]
102086 **$16.95**

Bitty Blossoms [Set of 1]
103536 **$16.95**

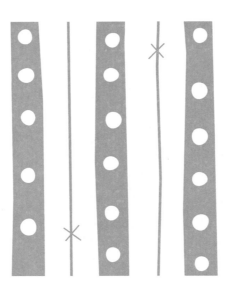

Filigree [Set of 1]
102784 **$16.95**

Groovy Lines [Set of 1]
100112 **$16.95**

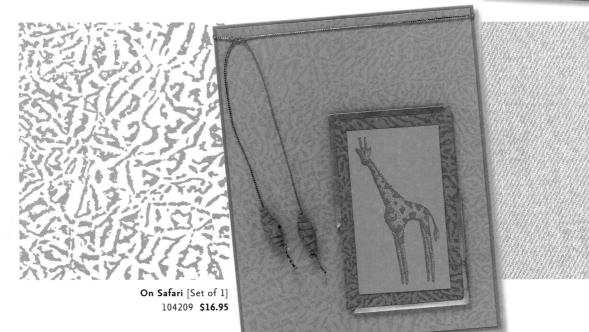

On Safari [Set of 1]
104209 **$16.95**

Just Jeans [Set of 1]
100259 **$16.95**

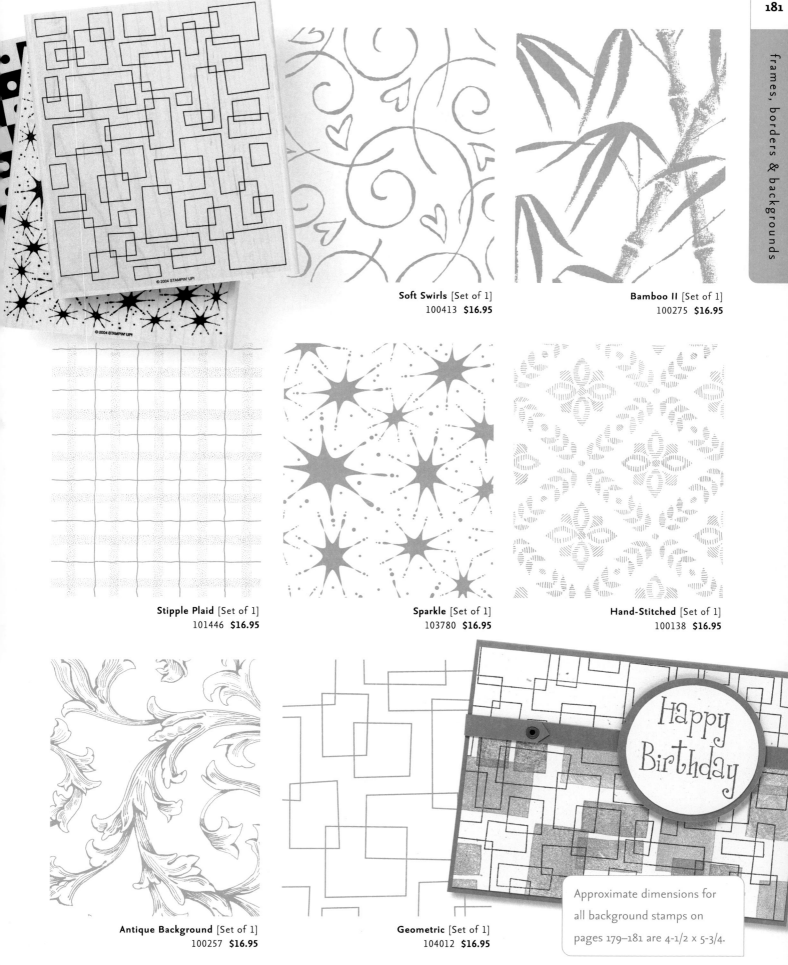

Soft Swirls [Set of 1]
100413 **$16.95**

Bamboo II [Set of 1]
100275 **$16.95**

Stipple Plaid [Set of 1]
101446 **$16.95**

Sparkle [Set of 1]
103780 **$16.95**

Hand-Stitched [Set of 1]
100138 **$16.95**

Antique Background [Set of 1]
100257 **$16.95**

Geometric [Set of 1]
104012 **$16.95**

Happy Birthday

Approximate dimensions for
all background stamps on
pages 179–181 are 4-1/2 x 5-3/4.

From the Heart

thinking OF YOU

it's your day!

hugs and kisses

a happy hello

PEACE

JOY

LOVE

Congratulations

warmest wishes

Happy Easter

many thanks

for you

merry & bright

Congratulations

All-Year Cheer I [Set of 12]
102189 **$29.95**

to:

from:

Celebrate!

HAPPY

Mother's Day

i miss you

you're invited

for: Jamie & Baby

on: May 8, 2004

at: 11:30 am

by: Katie & Amy

baby

HAPPY FATHER'S DAY

Happy Holidays

Happy Happy Birthday

You're a great friend!

for:

on:

at:

by:

baby

thank you very much

All-Year Cheer II [Set of 12]
102176 **$29.95**

Get Well Soon!

When everything is said and done, being sick is never fun!

Happy Birthday

However you may celebrate, whatever you may do— hope your day is filled with love and wishes that come true!

Thank You

Just a little note, Just a word or two— Thanking you for who you are And everything you do!

Best Wishes

Sharing in the happiness of your wonderful news!

Cheery Chat [Set of 8]
102856 **$28.95**

Happy *Wedding Day*

Congrats, Graduate

HAPPY Thanksgiving

Happy New Year!

Happy Anniversary

Merry Christmas

Happy St. Patrick's Day

good luck Happy Halloween

HAPPY *Valentine's Day*

just a note

to my mom

All-Year Cheer III [Set of 12]
101236 **$29.95**

CELEBRATE
TODAY!

BETTER GET BETTER

CELEBRATE TODAY!

I think of you

PERFECT FRIENDS

Simple Sayings [Set of 4]
102886 **$19.95**

HAPPY BIRtHDAY to you

thanks for your kindness

you make me smile

Just because

Simple Sayings II [Set of 4]
100174 **$19.95**

Celebrate

friendship

love

thank you

love

Wonderful Words [Set of 4]
103875 **$19.95**

CELEBRATE the SEASON

HUSBAND, WIFE...HAPPY LIFE!

welcome, little one

may hope fill your heart

Fun Phrases [Set of 4]
100134 **$19.95**

HUSBAND, WIFE...HAPPY LIFE!

happy new baby

For you	happy holidays	LeT iT snow!	Love you
Lucky you!	happy new baby	you make me smile!	you're a star!
Thanks a melon	give thanks	To: From:	you're invited

Tiny Talk [Set of 12]
103877 **$16.95**

I miss you

Thank you so much!

Happy Birthday

Have A Great Day!

Have A Great Day!

Vogue Verses [Set of 4]
101954 **$19.95**

YOU MAKE ME HAPPY!

.You take the cake!

i LOVE YOU MORE!

⋆ YOU'RE MY HERO! ⋆

YOU MAKE ME HAPPY!

You're my favorite!

Sassy Sayings I [Set of 4]
103903 **$19.95**

Just because I care!

I want to be you when I grow up!

Just what I wanted!

You take the cake!

H A P P Y · B I R T H D A Y

Sassy Sayings II [Set of 4]
103901 **$19.95**

To every thing there is a season, and a time to every purpose under the heaven.

—Ecclesiastes 3:1

My presence will go with thee, and I will give thee rest.

—Exodus 33:14

Trust in the Lord with all thine heart.

—Proverbs 3:5

God understands our prayers even when we can't find the words to say them.

—Author Unknown

Be still, and know that I am God.

—Psalms 46:10

Each one of us is God's special work of art.

Each one of us is God's special work of art.

—Joni Eareckson Tada

Words of Wisdom [Set of 6]
103957 **$19.95**

WITH *Sympathy*

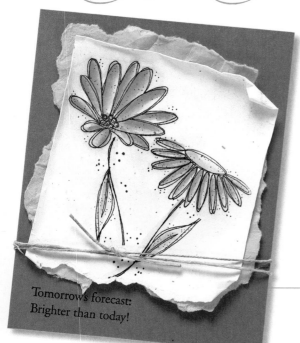

After the
showers,
the smell of
flowers.

Henry Van Dyke

The best thing
about the future is
that it comes only
one day at a time.

Abraham Lincoln

May the beautiful
memories that fill
your heart help to
bring you comfort.

Tomorrow's forecast:
Brighter than today!

Whatever happens,
God is there
to keep you safe
within his care.

Brighter Tomorrow [Set of 6]
104229 **$19.95**

Best Wishes

Happy Birthday

Thinking of You

Thank You

*Just a little note
to tell you
how special you are.*

*Sending sincere
thanks for your
thoughtfulness.*

*Thinking of you
on this special day
in a very warm
and loving way.*

*May happiness
be yours
today and always.*

Elegant Greetings [Set of 8]
101163 **$26.95**

Best wishes
on this
wonderful occasion!

Hoping that each day
finds you feeling
more and more
like your wonderful self!

May the simple
joys of life
fill this special day
and be yours throughout
the coming year.

Wishing you all
the love and happiness
two people can share.

Sending warmest wishes
for a future that will bring
all life's simple pleasures
and the best of everything!

Wishing you
merry days,
a heart that's light,
family and friends,
a season bright!

Your thoughtfulness
warms my heart
and brightens my day!

Just wanted you
to know
how special you are!

Versatile Verses [Set of 8]
102226 **$26.95**

Sending *warmest* wishes
for a *future* that will bring
all life's simple *pleasures*
and the *best* of everything!

Congrats! *Thanks*

Thinking

of You

Happy *Best*

Birthday *Wishes* *Get*

Good *Happy* *Well*

Luck! *Holidays* *Soon*

Happy Birthday

Bold & Basic Greetings [Set of 8]
102375 **$19.95**

DON'T MISS IT! This set has a coordinating Classy Brass®
embossing template sold on page 231.

SORRY I'M LATE—HOPE YOUR BIRTHDAY WAS GREAT!

WISHING YOU THE BEST TODAY AND ALWAYS!

Happy Birthday!

HAND-STAMPED ☆ BY

Horns to blow, and bright balloons, lots of presents, happy tunes!

I can't think of a nicer person to celebrate!

Ice cream, cake, and candles too—birthday wishes just for you!

May this birthday bring life's true gifts— good health, friendship, and love.

Happy Birthday

Happy Birthday!

Birthday Greetings [Set of 9]
102486 **$27.95**

Felicidades

¡Bienvenido Bebé!

GRACIAS

Para Tu Quinceañera

¡Qué Se Mejore Pronto!

Feliz Cumpleaños

Felicidades en su Matrimonio

Feliz Navidad

Saludos [Set of 8]
102617 **$19.95**

GREAT ★ NEW ★ ADDITIONS!

THANK YOU ♡ FOR YOUR BUSINESS!

For a great Hostess!

☆ Special ☆ ⊙ Offer! ☆

A gift for you!

Bring a friend!

I love what I do... You can too!

Thank You for your patience!

Business Memos [Set of 8]
102403 **$21.95**

stamped from the heart
© STAMPIN' UP!

hand-stamped with love
© STAMPIN' UP!

hand made
© STAMPIN' UP!

L O V E H A N D M A D E W I T H
© STAMPIN' UP!

Handmade with Love [Set of 4]
103016 **$11.95**

hand crafted
© STAMPIN' UP!

HAND STAMPED
© STAMPIN' UP!

stamp art
© STAMPIN' UP!

original design by:
© STAMPIN' UP!

ANGEL POLICY: Either of the Handmade with Love sets shown here fulfills the requirements of Stampin' Up!®'s angel policy, which governs the sale of hand-stamped items. Your demonstrator can give you full details.

Handmade with Love II [Set of 4]
102840 **$11.95**

Hey. Love

PaRTy

one

Thanks

little lizzy at

Lizzy was completely overwhelmed with all the attention she was given on her first birthday. We had a house full of guests. It took a while for us to convince her that it was okay to dig into the cake. After the first bite, she wouldn't let us take the cake away!

We are so blessed to have little Lizzy in our lives. Her first year has been filled with so many fun, new experiences.

July 19, 2003

PaRTy PaRTy PaRTy

DON'T MISS IT!
This set is also sold as part of a kit on page 25.

Word Play [Set of 6]
104167 **$19.95**

104064 Stampin' Around® **Confetti Play $5.95**
(Wheel only. Handle and ink cartridges sold separately. See pages 202–203, 228.)

great super
WON wonderful YEAH! WOO extraordinar
DER HOO! awesome
FUL! cool! WOW SUPER
FANTASTIC -incredible
neat friend

103753 Stampin' Around® Jumbo **Wonderful $7.95** (Wheel only. Handle and ink cartridges sold separately. See pages 202–203, 228.)

Add to your joy by counting your blessings.

Thinking of you.

How beautiful a day can be when kindness touches it.

—George Elliston

Thank You!

God writes the gospel not in the Bible alone, but on trees, and flowers, and clouds, and stars.

—Martin Luther

Sunshine in the heart not only warms thine own, but all that comes in contact with it.

—James T. Fields

Hope is the thing with feathers— That perches in the soul— And sings the tune without the words— And never stops—at all.

—Emily Dickinson

Count your life by smiles, not tears. Count your age by friends, not years.

Happy Birthday!

Friend to Friend [Set of 6]
103965 **$24.95**

How beautiful a day can be when kindness touches it.
—George Elliston

Merry Christmas

Happy Holidays

Season's Greetings

May your Holidays and New Year be filled with Happiness!

May love and laughter fill your season!

Thinking of you at this time of year, and though we are miles apart, may the special love that's sent your way keep us close at heart.

May Christmas bring carolers, holly and snow, bright twinkling lights upon your tree... popcorn for stringing and mistletoe, the warmth of friends and family.

Wishing you all the wonder, joy, and peace the season brings.

Season's Greetings [Set of 8]
100529 **$29.95**

Happy Holidays

Hangin' out with
a perfect day
me **&** my
How cute is that

Phrase Starters II [Set of 4]
104481 **$19.95**

DON'T MISS IT! See a sample
using this set on page 194.

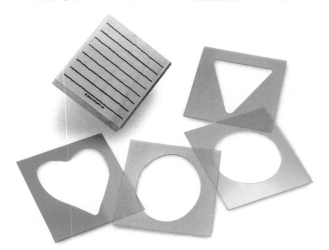

Just Journaling I [Set of 1 stamp and 4 templates]
100869 **$16.95**

Remember when

Thankful for

Memories of

Our Family

Elegant Beginnings [Set of 4]
101798 **$19.95**

DON'T MISS IT! See samples
using this set on pages 170–171.

Just Journaling II [Set of 1 stamp and 4 templates]
101995 **$16.95**

Journaling Fun [Set of 4]
102943 **$26.95**

day daughter grand my your Halloween sister thanks Christmas
laugh just boy " mother baby family all friend love
stamp party celebrate girl & son dream fall
father and brother ••• good little
for fun time summer birthday
peace winter hope special
imagine joy !
together wish spring
* valentine { happy best vacation
sweet favorite

Everyday Flexible Phrases* [Set of 56, 28 blocks]
104383 **$39.95**

alphabets

classic alphabet (See page 171 for sample.)

AaBbCcDd&'?!

double alphabet

Classic Alphabet [Set of 56 letters, 28 blocks]
104433 **$38.95**

0123#$(

Classic Alphabet Numbers [Set of 12]
104434 **$16.95**

Classic Caps [Set of 28]
104435 **$26.95**

With these alphabet sets, both upper- and lower-case letters are included. Mount them both on the same block for double the fun! Look for sets marked with this logo: **double alphabet**

simple type alphabet (See page 176 for sample.)

AaBbCc*?!*

double alphabet

Simple Type Alphabet* [Set of 56 letters, 28 blocks]
104207 **$38.95**

0123#$&

Simple Type Numbers* [Set of 12]
104205 **$16.95**

newsprint alphabet (See page 194 for sample.)

AaBbCc&?!

double alphabet

Newsprint Alphabet [Set of 56 letters, 28 blocks]
103961 **$38.95**

0123#(@

Newsprint Numbers [Set of 12]
104140 **$16.95**

all-around alphabet

AaBbCc?!;)

All-Around Alphabet [Set of 56 letters, 28 blocks]
104451 **$38.95**

double alphabet

DON'T MISS IT! This set has a coordinating Classy Brass® embossing template sold on page 231.

0123 # $

All-Around Alphabet Numbers [Set of 12]
104452 **$16.95**

brushstroke alphabet

AaBbCc?!"¿

Brushstroke Alphabet [Set of 56 letters, 28 blocks]
104438 **$38.95**

double alphabet

0123 $

Brushstroke Alphabet Numbers [Set of 12]
104439 **$16.95**

crayon fun alphabet

ABCD;)

Crayon Fun Alphabet Upper [Set of 28]
104440 **$26.95**

abcd?!

Crayon Fun Alphabet Lower [Set of 28]
104441 **$26.95**

0123 ♡ ☆

Crayon Fun Alphabet Numbers [Set of 12]
104442 **$16.95**

Lynn & Linda 3:04

FAMILY

To us **family** Means putting your arms Around each other and being there.

bold alphabet

AaBbCc?!")

Bold Alphabet [Set of 56 letters, 28 blocks]
104436 **$38.95**

double alphabet

0123#$

Bold Alphabet Numbers [Set of 12]
104437 **$16.95**

alphadots (See page 124 for sample.)

A B C D ! ?

Alphadots [Set of 28]
104042 **$26.95**

0 1 2 AND $ #

Alphadot Numbers [Set of 12]
103849 **$16.95**

contemporary alphabet (See page 78 for sample.)

Contemporary Alphabet [Set of 28]
104239 **$26.95**

Contemporary Alphabet Numbers [Set of 12]
104237 **$16.95**

alphabet fun

Alphabet Fun Upper [Set of 28]
104443 **$26.95**

Alphabet Fun Lower [Set of 28]
104444 **$26.95**

Alphabet Fun Numbers [Set of 12]
104445 **$16.95**

TRY THIS! Our large layering Circle and Square punches on page 222 are a perfect complement to our alphabet sets. The Concave and Convex Square punches are sized to work with smaller alphabets such as the Simple Type, Classic, and Brushstroke Alphabets. Use the 1/2-inch Circle punch with the Alphadots set.

crazy alphabet

Crazy Alphabet [Set of 28]
104453 **$26.95**

Crazy Alphabet Numbers [Set of 12]
104454 **$16.95**

say it with stamps

pure & simple alphabet (See page 191 for sample.)

ABCD?!

Pure & Simple Alphabet Upper [Set of 28]
104455 **$26.95**

abcd&)

Pure & Simple Alphabet Lower [Set of 28]
104456 **$26.95**

0123#$

Pure & Simple Alphabet Numbers [Set of 12]
104457 **$16.95**

quirky alphabet

ABCD?!

Quirky Alphabet Upper [Set of 28]
104458 **$26.95**

abcd);

Quirky Alphabet Lower [Set of 28]
104459 **$26.95**

012&♥★

Quirky Alphabet Numbers [Set of 12]
104460 **$16.95**

---

new journaling fonts!

Write Me a Memory® Journaling Font CDs: Volume I & Volume II

Contains exclusive fonts offering the ease and flexibility of computer journaling while providing the handwritten look that makes each page feel unique and personal. English only | En anglais seulement

System Requirements: PC—Windows 95 or higher, Pentium/equivalent or higher; Macintosh—Macintosh Power PC Processor, System 8.5 or higher

[VOLUME I]

DECO SERIF
FARMER J
Favero Wide
Heritage
Carefree Kelly
casual LiesLJ
CSS Hand Pittipat

[VOLUME II]

CONTEMPO CAPS
Girly Girl
Harry Paul
JODYOLA
KP Quick Passing Notes
Little Lamb Steele Script
marker j low Woodward Script

Write Me a Memory® Journaling Fonts CD: Volume I [10 fonts]
100482 **$14.95**

new! Write Me a Memory® Journaling Fonts CD: Volume II [10 fonts]
104368 **$14.95**

personalized stamps

Stamp your personal belongings and correspondence with Stampin' Up!'s personalized stamps. You can create personal stationery, desktop memo sheets, address labels, and more! Personalized stamps must be ordered on special forms. Please ask your demonstrator for assistance. (*Please note: No returns can be accepted on personalized stamps.*)

a. text-only stamps

- Up to 32 characters per line (spaces count as a character)
- Capitals count as 2 spaces
- Choose from 1–4 lines of text

b. text-and-image stamps

- Up to 32 characters per line (spaces count as a character)
- Capitals count as 2 spaces
- Choose either 3 or 4 lines of text
- Font styles and images cannot be interchanged

c. "hand stamped by" stamps

- One line of personalized text (for name)
- Your name is in all caps
- Up to 16 capital letters for name (spaces count as a character)

d. large text-only stamps

- Up to 16 characters per line (spaces count as a character)
- Capitals count as 2 spaces
- Choose either 1 or 2 lines of text

a. text-only stamps

First & Last Name
1234 Your Street
City, State 12345
(123) 456-7890

104541	Classic One-Line	$9.95
104540	Classic Two-Line	$12.95
104539	Classic Three-Line	$16.95
104538	Classic Four-Line	$19.95

First & Last Name
1234 Your Street
City, State 12345
(123) 456-7890

104545	Contemporary One-Line	$9.95
104544	Contemporary Two-Line	$12.95
104543	Contemporary Three-Line	$16.95
104542	Contemporary Four-Line	$19.95

First & Last Name
1234 Your Street
City, State 12345
(123) 456-7890

104549	Script One-Line	$9.95
104548	Script Two-Line	$12.95
104547	Script Three-Line	$16.95
104546	Script Four-Line	$19.95

b. text-and-image stamps

First & Last Name
1234 Your Street
City, State 12345
(123) 456-7890

| 104533 | Best Bee Three-Line | $17.95 |
| 104532 | Best Bee Four-Line | $19.95 |

First & Last Name
1234 Your Street
City, State 12345
(123) 456-7890

| 104529 | Elegant Flower Three-Line | $17.95 |
| 104528 | Elegant Flower Four-Line | $19.95 |

First & Last Name
1234 Your Street
City, State 12345
(123) 456-7890

| 104531 | Playful Confetti Three-Line | $17.95 |
| 104530 | Playful Confetti Four-Line | $19.95 |

c. "hand stamped by" stamps

YOUR NAME HERE
COPYRIGHT STAMPIN' UP!

| 103516 | Tag It | $17.95 |

Hand Stamped by
YOUR NAME HERE
© Stampin' Up!

| 104534 | On a Whim | $17.95 |

HAND STAMPED BY
YOUR NAME HERE
© STAMPIN' UP!

| 104535 | Decorative Design | $17.95 |

ANGEL POLICY The "Hand Stamped By" Personalized Name Stamps shown above fulfill the requirements of Stampin' Up!'s angel policy, which governs the sale of hand-stamped items. Your demonstrator can give you full details.

d. large text-only stamps

| 104536 | Simple Serif One-Line* | $12.95 |
| 104537 | Simple Serif Two-Line* | $14.95 |

Name Here
(123) 456-7890

Happy Holidays
from Jan Smith

Color families

[48 FABULOUS COLORS]

EARTH ELEMENTS COLOR FAMILY

BOLD BRIGHTS COLOR FAMILY

 card stock

Stampin' Up!'s quality card stock is dyed with pure color all the way through. Ideal for scrapbooking, this acid- and lignin-free card stock offers all sorts of stamping and scrapbooking options, from a simple background paper to the core elements of stunning cards and other stamping projects. It comes in both 12 x 12 and 8-1/2 x 11. See pages 202–203.

stamp pads

Stampin' Up!'s revolutionary pads feature a patented, flip-top design that stores the inking surface upside-down, so the pad surface stays juicy between re-inkings. See pages 202–203.

Our **Craft Stampin' Pads** contain rich pigment inks that are ideal for scrapbooking, embossing, and other craft projects—they're your best choice for long-lasting color. Be sure to order a matching refill to keep your Craft Pad moist.

Our award-winning **Classic Stampin' Pads** feature our popular, fast-drying, dye-based inks. Acid free.

standard   jumbo

stampin' around cartridges

Fast and fun, Stampin' Around wheels are perfect for borders and backgrounds, and now you can choose from 2 sizes! Our jumbo wheels and cartridges add a new element to Stampin' Around. The larger images provide additional creative options for your quick-and-easy projects. Our Stampin' Around line also offers beautiful, fun, and easy color coordination. Stampin' Around standard and jumbo ink cartridges come in Stampin' Up!'s exclusive colors to coordinate with card stock, ink pads, and markers. Color made easy meets stamping made easy!

Refill with Classic ink refills. Acid free. 1/2 oz. Handles are sold separately and are available on page 228. Empty cell cartridges are also available on page 228 and embossing cartridges are available on page 230.

classic stampin' spots®

These 1-inch-square ink pads are an affordable way to access all of our colors for your creative genius. These pads use the same ink as the full-size Classic Stampin' Pads, so they coordinate with our exclusive card stock, pastels, markers, and other fun accessories. They're a wonderful way to sample our colors. See pages 202–203.

ink refills

You'll want a refill for each of your ink pads, and you can now order your Classic ink refills packaged in our own Stampin' Up! color families. (You can still order both Craft and Classic ink refills individually.) And when you order an entire set, you receive a discount of more than $2! You can also use the Classic ink refills to fill your Stampin' Around cartridges and re-ink your Spectrum Pads. Acid free. 1/2 oz. See pages 202–203.

[COLORS, ITEM NUMBERS & PRICES ARE LISTED ON PAGES 202–203]

stampin' write markers

With a cap design exclusive to Stampin' Up!, these markers feature a fine tip for details and writing and a brush tip for wider color applications. Each marker is like getting 2 long-lasting markers in 1! Acid-free, water-based, dye ink. See pages 202–203 to purchase markers individually.

Many Marvelous Markers   Set of 48 Stampin' Write® dual-tip markers. Horizontal storage case keeps both tips evenly inked.

100087 Many Marvelous Markers	**$119.95**

stampin' write journalers

new! *sm* Fade-resistant, waterproof, pigment markers ideal for journaling and scrapbooking. Now in 9 of our 48 colors. Black tip sizes: .6mm, .8mm, and 2.3mm bullet, and brush. Color tip sizes: .6mm and 2.3mm bullet. See pages 202–203.

color coach®

This tool provides guidelines for creating great color combinations with our exclusive color palette. Even a beginner can combine colors like an experienced designer for professional results. It's color made easy!

101513 Color Coach	**$9.95**

stampin' pastels

Delight your color sense with these refillable pastels. Protected in a sturdy case complete with 6 applicators and an eraser. Each color family refill assortment includes 4 colors of chalk. Acid free.

102516	Stampin' Pastels®	**$24.95**
103174	Applicator Refill (15)	**$2.95**
100852	Pastel Erasers (2)	**$2.50**
100241	Bold Brights 1 Refill (Brilliant Blue, Glorious Green, Lovely Lilac, Real Red)	**$3.95**
100242	Bold Brights 2 Refill (Green Galore, Pink Passion, Only Orange, Yoyo Yellow)	**$3.95**
100243	Bold Brights 3 Refill (Gable Green, Orchid Opulence, Positively Pink, Tempting Turquoise)	**$3.95**
100238	Earth Elements 1 Refill (Creamy Caramel, More Mustard, Old Olive, Ruby Red)	**$3.95**
100239	Earth Elements 2 Refill (Basic Black, Close to Cocoa, Garden Green, Really Rust)	**$3.95**
100240	Earth Elements 3 Refill (Cameo Coral, Chocolate Chip, Going Gray, Summer Sun)	**$3.95**
100232	Rich Regals 1 Refill (Ballet Blue, Baroque Burgundy, Forest Foliage, Night of Navy)	**$3.95**
100233	Rich Regals 2 Refill (Bordering Blue, Eggplant Envy, Not Quite Navy, Rose Red)	**$3.95**
100234	Rich Regals 3 Refill (Brocade Blue, Marvelous Magenta, Rose Romance, Taken with Teal)	**$3.95**
100235	Soft Subtles 1 Refill (Barely Banana, Bliss Blue, Mellow Moss, Pretty in Pink)	**$3.95**
100236	Soft Subtles 2 Refill (Blush Blossom, Lavender Lace, Perfect Plum, Sage Shadow)	**$3.95**
100237	Soft Subtles 3 Refill (Almost Amethyst, Mauve Mist, Mint Melody, Pale Plum)	**$3.95**
102476	Real Red Refill	**$1.50**
102575	White Refill	**$1.50**

DON'T MISS THESE OTHER PRODUCTS THAT COME IN A SELECTION OF OUR 48 COLORS

Colored Vellum (p. 205)	Die-Cut Boxes & Tags (p. 219–220)
Tag Sheets (p. 219)	Spectrum Pads (p. 226)
Vellum Tag Sheets (p. 219)	Eyelets (p. 233)
Pennant Sheets (p. 219)	Buttons (p. 234)

accessories

bold brights

bold brights	classic stampin' pad $4.95	classic ink refill $2.50	stampin' write marker $2.95	stampin' write journaler $2.95	craft stampin' pad $6.95	craft ink refill $3.95	8-1/2 x 11 card stock (24 sheets) $4.50	12 x 12 card stock (20 sheets) $6.50	Stampin' Around cartridge[d] $4.95	Stampin' Around jumbo cartridge[d] $6.95
brilliant blue	100691	100763	100057	–	101843	103006	100721	102164	100871	103674
gable green	101673	101483	100049	–	101671	101232	102795	101405	102117	–
glorious green	103040	101453	100047	–	101436	100434	101697	102613	102212	103676
green galore	102122	101735	100048	–	101325	102772	101768	100544	100802	–
lovely lilac	102874	103077	100056	104177	102965	101695	100427	101601	101256	103677
only orange	102696	102931	100051	–	101951	102111	102837	102009	101366	–
orchid opulence	101859	101324	100055	–	101900	100464	100969	101941	100809	–
pink passion	101212	102308	100053	–	102916	103036	102762	102615	102667	–
positively pink	103122	100944	100054	–	101157	101630	100734	101386	101725	–
real red	103133	103287	100052	104173	101190	102104	102482	101554	102996	103675
tempting turquoise	100814	101041	100058	–	100741	100957	102067	103208	101199	–
yoyo yellow	102717	101986	100050	–	101608	103325	102824	101786	102361	–

earth elements

earth elements	classic stampin' pad $4.95	classic ink refill $2.50	stampin' write marker $2.95	stampin' write journaler $2.95 / $4.95 (black*)	craft stampin' pad $6.95	craft ink refill $3.95	8-1/2 x 11 card stock (24 sheets) $4.50	12 x 12 card stock (20 sheets) $6.50	Stampin' Around cartridge[d] $4.95	Stampin' Around jumbo cartridge[d] $6.95
basic black	101179[b]	102512[b]	100082	102634	102192	102995	102851	100856	104581[b]	104582[b]
cameo coral	103035	102238	100074	–	101933	101033	100475	100508	102785	–
chocolate chip	100908	101065	100071	–	101816	102847	102128	100623	102496	–
close to cocoa	103139	102444	100072	–	100549	100925	101341	101316	100714	–
creamy caramel	103220	101478	100078	–	103034	102004	102514	103302	100654	103671
garden green	102272	102059	100080	–	101841	100519	102584	102651	103252	–
going gray	103274	102521	100081	–	102669	103136	103154	100939	101821	–
more mustard	103162	101962	100076	104176	103092	101990	100946	101566	100566	103672
old olive	102277	100531	100079	104175	103063	101425	100702	101556	102021	103670
really rust	102549	100685	100073	–	102437	103014	100661	100470	102927	–
ruby red	102259	100532	100075	–	101009	102448	102030	103030	102047	103673
summer sun	100537	101231	100077	–	101690	102765	103124	102480	100660	–

assorted

assorted	classic stampin' pads (set of 12)[c] $54.95	classic ink refills (set of 12) $27.95	stampin' write markers (set of 12, includes small storage case) $29.95	classic stampin' spots (set of 12) $21.50	craft stampin' pads (set of 12)[c] $76.95		8-1/2 x 11 card stock (36 sheets, 3 ea. of 12 colors) $6.95	12 x 12 card stock (24 sheets, 2 ea. of 12 colors) $7.95		
bold brights	101876	104192	100084	102387	101747	–	101847	101884	–	–
earth elements	102923	104191	100086	103240	102804	–	103060	102495	–	–
rich regals	100465	104190	100085	103116	100454	–	103340	101228	–	–
soft subtles	102542	104189	100083	101968	100819	–	101612	102243	–	–

rich regals	classic stampin' pad $4.95	classic ink refill $2.50	stampin' write marker $2.95	stampin' write journaler $2.95	craft stampin' pad $6.95	craft ink refill $3.95	8-1/2 x 11 card stock (24 sheets) $4.50	12 x 12 card stock (20 sheets) $6.50	Stampin' Around cartridge[d] $4.95	Stampin' Around jumbo cartridge[d] $6.95
ballet blue	100907	101713	100066	104179	102855	101732	100613	102899	102305	103662
baroque burgundy	102579	103193	100062	104178	101250	101309	102398	101696	100806	103663
bordering blue	102265	100940	100070	–	101374	102530	102630	101733	101186	–
brocade blue	101102	100408	100064	–	101593	100788	101166	101742	103198	–
eggplant envy	102924	101197	100060	–	102523	102053	100749	102050	102409	
forest foliage	101914	101108	100061	–	103155	101546	102365	102594	100722	103665
marvelous magenta	101283	101388	100067	–	102348	102232	102792	103097	102123	–
night of navy	102977	103033	100069	–	103181	103131	100867	100653	103027	103664
not quite navy	103008	102949	100059	–	103227	102310	101722	102443	103084	–
rose red	101778	102109	100063	–	101545	102915	102544	102327	100520	–
rose romance	102092	102519	100065	–	101539	101191	101991	101724	101112	–
taken with teal	103257	100550	100068		100617	102049	101584	101176	100460	

soft subtles	classic stampin' pad $4.95	classic ink refill $2.50	stampin' write marker $2.95	stampin' write journaler $2.95	craft stampin' pad $6.95	craft ink refill $3.95	8-1/2 x 11 card stock (24 sheets) $4.50	12 x 12 card stock (20 sheets) $6.50	Stampin' Around cartridge[d] $4.95	Stampin' Around jumbo cartridge[d] $6.95
almost amethyst	101723	102580	100043	–	101211	102282	102158	100704	100659	–
barely banana	101170	100639	100039	–	101609	101676	102701	101929	101516	–
bliss blue	100769	101765	100046	–	100960	101138	100510	102665	101314	103669
blush blossom	102609	100614	100037	–	102080	100935	103318	102814	101678	–
lavender lace	101305	100862	100041	–	103144	101590	101614	100905	101812	
mauve mist	102618	102731	100042	–	102699	100451	102901	101762	102861	–
mellow moss	102774	101771	100038	–	101054	101967	102898	100638	102871	103667
mint melody	101318	102339	100044	–	101215	100705	102932	102431	101056	–
pale plum	102732	101268	100036	104174	103271	102202	101658	101615	101519	–
perfect plum	101437	102107	100035	–	102869	100697	101889	101281	101139	103666
pretty in pink	101301	102295	100045	–	100857	101127	100459	101448	100562	103668
sage shadow	102532	100720	100040	104180	103251	100711	101563	101815	101475	–

neutrals	classic stampin' pad $4.95	classic ink refill $2.50			craft stampin' pad $6.95	craft ink refill $3.95	8-1/2 x 11 card stock (40 sheets) $6.50	12 x 12 card stock (20 sheets) $5.95	Stampin' Around cartridge & refill $9.95	Stampin' Around cartridge refill only $5.50
white	–	–	–	–	101731	101780	100730	101874	101460	103017
vanilla	–	–	–	–	104308	104328	101650	100467	–	–
basic brown	104315[b]	104314[b]	–	–	–	–	–	–	–	–

[a] The Basic Black Stampin' Write Journalers include 2 markers. All other colors include 1. See tip sizes on page 201. The Basic Black Stampin' Write Journalers come in a sturdy plastic storage case.
[b] The Basic Brown and Basic Black Classic ink is waterproof and will not bleed.
[c] Comes with sturdy cardboard storage case.
[d] Use Classic Stampin' Ink Refills for your Stampin' Around ink cartridges and jumbo cartridges.

neutral card stock

Ultrasmooth White · Ultrasmooth Vanilla · Kraft · Naturals Ivory · Naturals White

confetti card stock

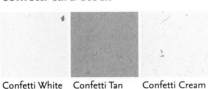

Confetti White · Confetti Tan · Confetti Cream

specialty card stock

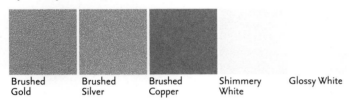

Brushed Gold · Brushed Silver · Brushed Copper · Shimmery White · Glossy White

velveteen paper

▧ neutral card stock

8-1/2 x 11 Card Stock 40 sheets per pkg. ⓐ❶ⓑ

100730	Ultrasmooth White	**$6.50**
101650	Ultrasmooth Vanilla	**$6.50**
102125	Kraft	**$6.50**
101849	Naturals Ivory	**$6.50**
102316	Naturals White	**$6.50**

12 x 12 Card Stock 20 sheets per pkg. ⓐ❶ⓑ

101874	Ultrasmooth White	**$5.95**
100467	Ultrasmooth Vanilla	**$5.95**
101119	Kraft	**$5.95**
102353	Naturals Ivory	**$5.95**
102841	Naturals White	**$5.95**

▧ confetti card stock

8-1/2 x 11 Card Stock 40 sheets per pkg. ⓐ❶ⓑ

102028	Confetti White	**$7.95**
101376	Confetti Tan	**$7.95**
102835	Confetti Cream	**$7.95**

12 x 12 Card Stock 20 sheets per pkg. ⓐ❶ⓑ

102313	Confetti White	**$7.50**
102417	Confetti Tan	**$7.50**
101409	Confetti Cream	**$7.50**

specialty card stock

8-1/2 x 11 Card Stock 10 sheets per pkg. unless otherwise noted

102935	Brushed Gold ⓐ	**$6.95**
100712	Brushed Silver ⓐ	**$6.95**
new! 103975	Brushed Copper ⓐ	**$6.95**
101910	Shimmery White	**$6.95**
102599	Glossy White (25 sheets)	**$4.95**

velveteen paper

Stamp this soft paper to create a look of stamped velvet, or use it to add an elegant accent. 6 sheets, 1 of ea. color shown. 9 x 12

102157	Velveteen Paper Assortment	**$12.95**

layering helper

Layer Ease These little discs enable you to cut perfect mats for your photos and art in any shape you desire. So quick and easy, you can take layering to a whole new level! Achieve perfect 1/8-inch, 1/4-inch, 3/8-inch, or 1/2-inch mats with ease. Pencil not included.

100683	Layer Ease	**$13.50**

ⓐ = acid free   ❶ = lignin free   ⓑ = buffered

ⓈⓂ vellum card stock & paper

White Vellum 8-1/2 x 11 includes 20 sheets per pkg. 12 x 12 includes 12 sheets per pkg. ⓐ ❶

101856	8-1/2 x 11 Card Stock	$6.50
101839	8-1/2 x 11 Paper	$4.95
103598	12 x 12 Paper	$6.95

Printed Vellum Exclusive Stampin' Up! images, overlaid on fine translucent vellum, make these white-on-white papers an elegant choice! 8-1/2 x 11. 10 sheets per pkg. ⓐ ❶

100965	Snowflakes Paper	$5.95
101326	Swirls Paper	$5.95

Colored Vellum Stamp on these colored vellums, layer them with card stock, or partner them with ribbon, eyelets, brads, or our Designer Series paper for a look that's sure to catch people's eyes. 12 x 12. 3 sheets of each color listed at right. ⓐ ❶

103594	Bold Brights	$6.95
103597	Earth Elements	$6.95
103596	Rich Regals	$6.95
103595	Soft Subtles	$6.95

mulberry paper

Mulberry papers come in colors that work beautifully with Stampin' Up!'s exclusive color-coordinated papers, markers, and ink pads. 8-1/2 x 11. Assortments include 10 sheets, 2 ea. of 5 colors.

102370	Brights	$6.95
100860	Earths	$6.95
101693	Regals	$6.95
102253	Subtles	$6.95
102678	White (5 sheets)	$3.95

vellum card stock & paper

white   snowflakes   swirls

bold brights: Brilliant Blue, Glorious Green, Lovely Lilac, Real Red

earth elements: Creamy Caramel, More Mustard, Old Olive, Ruby Red

rich regals: Ballet Blue, Baroque Burgundy, Forest Foliage, Night of Navy

soft subtles: Barely Banana, Bliss Blue, Mellow Moss, Pretty in Pink

mulberry paper

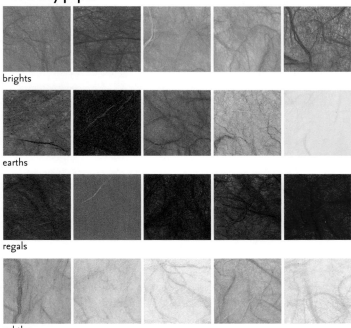

brights

earths

regals

subtles

white

envelope size key

mini (3 x 4-1/8)

small (3-5/8 x 5-1/8)

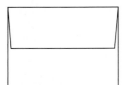

medium (4-3/8 x 5-3/4)

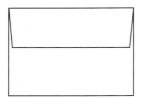

large (4-3/4 x 6-1/2)

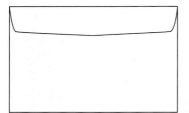

extra large (5-3/4 x 8-3/4)

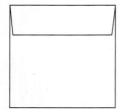

medium square (5-1/2 x 5-1/2)

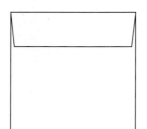

large square (6-1/2 x 6-1/2)

gift cards with mini scalloped envelopes

DON'T MISS IT!
Our medium envelope fits our standard card size (4-1/4 x 5-1/2).

raised edge note cards with small envelopes

colored translucent medium envelopes

large square white vellum envelopes

envelopes

Mini Scalloped Envelopes (sold with cards below)

Small Envelopes (sold with cards below)

Medium 4-3/8 x 5-3/4 Sized for a standard quarter-page card. Amounts per package listed in parentheses below.

101787	Ultrasmooth White (40)	**$5.95**
102293	Ultrasmooth Vanilla (40)	**$5.95**
102044	Kraft (40)	**$5.95**
103234	Naturals Ivory (40)	**$5.95**
101640	Naturals White (40)	**$5.95**
102631	Confetti White (40)	**$7.95**
101706	Confetti Tan (40)	**$7.95**
102610	Confetti Cream (40)	**$7.95**
102208	Shimmery White (20)	**$4.95**
102075	White Vellum (20)	**$7.95**
sm 102619	Clear Translucent* (50)	**$4.95**
sm 101495	Colored Translucent* (10 ea. of 5 colors)	**$7.50**

Large 4-3/4 x 6-1/2. 40 per pkg.

101074	Ultrasmooth White	**$6.50**
101701	Ultrasmooth Vanilla	**$6.50**

Extra Large Sized for cards made with a folded sheet of 8-1/2 x 11 card stock. 5-3/4 x 8-3/4. 20 per pkg.

101097	Ultrasmooth White*	**$4.95**

Medium Square 5-1/2 x 5-1/2. 20 per pkg.

102219	Ultrasmooth White*	**$5.95**

new! **Large Square** Sized for a 6 x 6 brag book page. 6-1/2 x 6-1/2. 10 per pkg.

104200	White Vellum*	**$6.95**

cards & envelopes

Gift Cards with Mini Scalloped Envelopes Card size: 2-3/4 x 3-7/8. 20 per pkg.

101307	Ultrasmooth White	**$4.95**

Note Cards with Small Envelopes Card size: 3-1/2 x 5. 20 per pkg.

101950	Ultrasmooth White	**$4.95**

Raised Edge Note Cards with Small Envelopes Card size: 3-3/8 x 4-7/8. 20 per pkg.

101264	Ultrasmooth White	**$4.95**
102909	Ultrasmooth Vanilla	**$4.95**

Greeting Cards with Medium Envelopes Card size: 4-1/4 x 5-1/2. 20 per pkg.

101721	Ultrasmooth White	**$5.95**
103129	Confetti Cream	**$6.95**
102900	Confetti Tan	**$6.95**
102014	Confetti White	**$6.95**

Square Cards with Medium Square Envelopes Card size: 5-1/4 x 5-1/4. 10 per pkg.

102275	Ultrasmooth White*	**$6.95**

* Requires extra postage

templates & stencils

Shapes Designed by Stampin' Up!, these stencils coordinate with popular Stampin' Up! images. Use for scrapbooking and papercrafting. All templates and stencils are made of durable, translucent white plastic. 10 x 12. For convenient access and organization, store in 12 x 12 Craft Keepers shown on page 223.

101885	Journaling	$4.50
100818	Celebrations	$4.50
101472	Hearts & Stars	$4.50
100647	Nature	$4.50
100834	Basic Shapes	$4.50
102753	Stripes	$4.50
101175	Seasonal Shapes I	$4.50
101272	Seasonal Shapes II	$4.50
101808	Cloud, Moon & Stars (9-1/8 x 7-3/8)	$4.50

Plaidmaker™ Made with the same durable plastic as our other templates and stencils, these templates can be used with a foam brayer or sponge to create custom plaids in any color combination. 2 templates in each set. Notched to hold 12 x 12 card stock; works with 8-1/2 x 11 too!

102338	Large Plaidmaker	$11.95
102697	Small Plaidmaker	$11.95

Envelope Template Assortments Sets of 3.

103269	Assortment I	$12.50
100770	Assortment II	$12.50

new! **Mini Envelope Template** 5 designs. 8-1/2 x 11

104104	Mini Envelope Template	$5.95

shapes

journaling

celebrations

hearts & stars

nature

basic shapes

stripes

seasonal shapes I

seasonal shapes II

cloud, moon & stars

plaidmakers

large plaidmaker (pair)

small plaidmaker (pair)

envelope templates

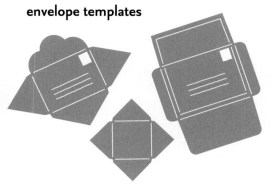
Assortment I: small, small square, and large

Assortment II: medium square, gift, and medium

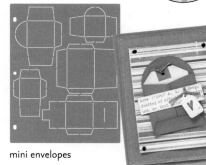
mini envelopes

designer series paper & vellum

Paper Sized for 12 x 12 scrapbooks, you can easily cut the sheets down for 8-1/2 x 11 scrapbooks, smaller brag book pages, or cards. 12 sheets, 2 of ea. design. ⓐ ⓵ ⓑ

102204	Candy	$5.95
102076	Splash	$5.95
101067	Tudor	$5.95
102335	Victorian	$5.95
103655	Tickles	$5.95
103656	Pickles	$5.95
103658	Sweet	$5.95
103657	Sassy	$5.95
new! 104136	Pool Party	$5.95
new! 104135	Slumber Party	$5.95
new! 104133	Copper Kiss	$5.95
new! 104134	Silver Bliss	$5.95

Vellum Terrific designs based on Stampin' Up!'s exclusive Designer Series paper! 12 x 12. 12 sheets, 2 of ea. design. ⓐ ⓵

102037	Candy	$9.95
102034	Splash	$9.95
102944	Tudor	$9.95
101145	Victorian	$9.95
103651	Tickles	$9.95
103652	Pickles	$9.95
103654	Sweet	$9.95
103653	Sassy	$9.95
new! 104132	Pool Party	$9.95
new! 104131	Slumber Party	$9.95
new! 104129	Copper Kiss	$9.95
new! 104130	Silver Bliss	$9.95

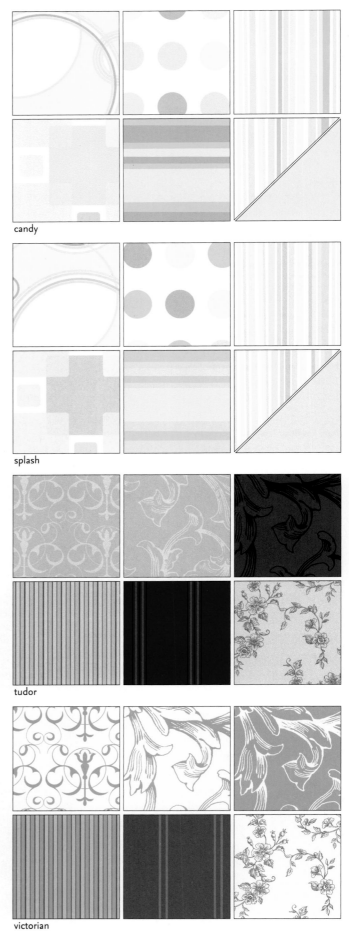

candy

splash

tudor

victorian

ⓐ = acid free   ⓵ = lignin free   ⓑ = buffered   © 1990–2004 Stampin' Up!

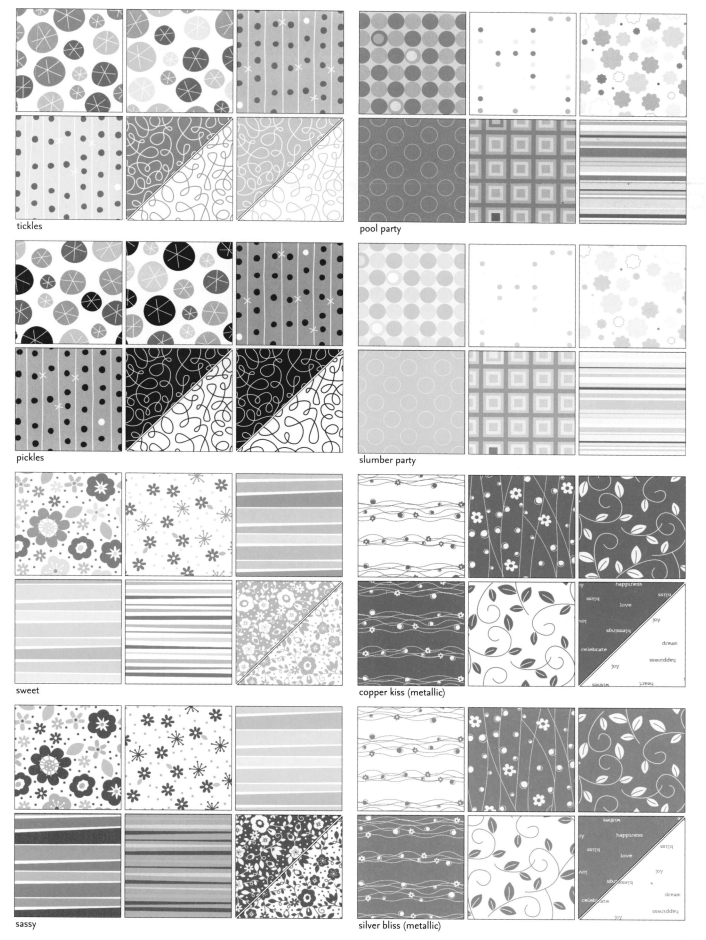

tickles

pickles

sweet

sassy

pool party

slumber party

copper kiss (metallic)

silver bliss (metallic)

All patterns are shown at 50%. Swatches that are split are different in the paper and vellum packages. The top swatch represents paper and the bottom swatch represents the vellum.

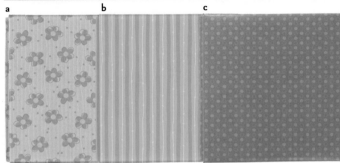

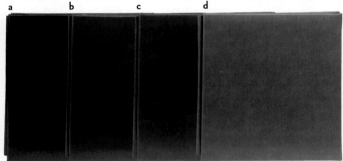

designer post albums

Albums feature exclusive Stampin' Up! art on the cover. Includes 10 page protectors.

a. Love without End

103700	6 x 6 Brag Book	**$19.95**
103699	8-1/2 x 11	**$24.95**
103698	12 x 12	**$29.95**

b. Groovy Lines

103694	6 x 6 Brag Book	**$19.95**
103693	8-1/2 x 11	**$24.95**
103692	12 x 12	**$29.95**

c. By Design

103697	6 x 6 Brag Book	**$19.95**
103696	8-1/2 x 11	**$24.95**
103695	12 x 12	**$29.95**

classic leather post albums

High-quality bonded leather. Includes 10 page protectors.

a. Black

new!	104188	6 x 6 Brag Book	**$24.95**
	100700	8-1/2 x 11	**$34.95**
	102782	12 x 12	**$39.95**

b. Burgundy

new!	104187	6 x 6 Brag Book	**$24.95**
	101594	8-1/2 x 11	**$34.95**
	100786	12 x 12	**$39.95**

c. Forest

new!	104185	6 x 6 Brag Book	**$24.95**
	103082	8-1/2 x 11	**$34.95**
	103338	12 x 12	**$39.95**

d. Pecan

new!	104186	6 x 6 Brag Book	**$24.95**
	102597	8-1/2 x 11	**$34.95**
	101394	12 x 12	**$39.95**

page protectors, post

These styles are specially designed to lie flat in our post-bound albums.
3 cardboard spacers and 3 post extenders included. Polypropylene. 20 per pkg.

103687	6 x 6	**$5.95**
103145	8-1/2 x 11	**$6.95**
100670	12 x 12	**$9.95**

Post Extenders 12 per pkg. (not shown)

new! 104184	Post Extenders	**$5.95**

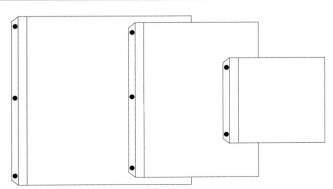

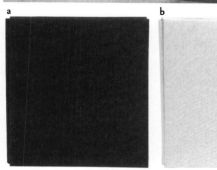

a   b

a   b

new! sm classic linen post albums

Our new linen albums are a great option for scrapbookers who want a classy, high-quality album! These beautiful albums come in 3 sizes and are designed for long-lasting durability. Includes 10 page protectors.

a. Navy

104516	6 x 6 Brag Book	**$19.95**
104517	8-1/2 x 11	**$24.95**
104518	12 x 12	**$29.95**

b. Natural

104515	6 x 6 Brag Book	**$19.95**
104520	8-1/2 x 11	**$24.95**
104519	12 x 12	**$29.95**

new! sm classic linen ring albums

Another option in our new linen finish. The 12 x 12 and 8-1/2 x 11 albums feature three 1-1/2-inch straight D rings. The 6 x 6 album features two 1-inch straight D rings. Includes 10 page protectors.

a. Navy

104512	6 x 6 Brag Book	**$16.95**
104513	8-1/2 x 11	**$21.95**
104514	12 x 12	**$26.95**

b. Natural

104509	6 x 6 Brag Book	**$16.95**
104510	8-1/2 x 11	**$21.95**
104511	12 x 12	**$26.95**

new! sm page protectors, ring

Select this option for protecting your scrapbook pages when using our ring albums. Available without the side gusset provided for post-bound albums, these polypropylene page protectors offer the same roominess and high quality you depend on from all Stampin' Up! page protectors. 20 per pkg.

104521	6 x 6	**$5.95**
104523	8-1/2 x 11	**$6.95**
104522	12 x 12	**$9.95**

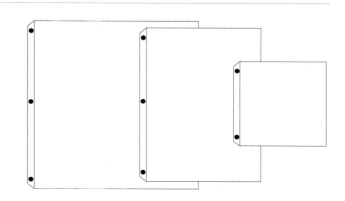

simply scrappin' kits

Our Simply Scrappin' kits have been redesigned and reconfigured to be better than ever! Every kit features the new format with self-adhesive punchouts and contains 18 sheets of coordinating materials to create distinctive scrapbook pages: 8 sheets of 12 x 12 solid-color card stock; 4 sheets of 12 x 12 patterned card stock; 6 sheets of 6 x 12 self-adhesive punchouts featuring exclusive images and Quick Strips. In addition, all sheets can be easily trimmed to create 8-1/2 x 11 and 6 x 6 pages. Acid & lignin free.

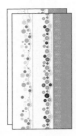  

Designed to coordinate with our Designer Series paper and vellum, these full-color images make quick and easy borders, journaling boxes, or page accents. Combine with Stampin' Up!'s alphabet stamp sets to make incredible page titles. Contains 6 sheets of self-adhesive Quick Strips (6 x 12).

new! Simply Scrappin' **Quick Strips**
104369 **$6.95**

Kara's Smile

I just love how Kara's eyes light up every time she smiles. Kara is a happy girl and is always full of giggles. She is a joy to have in our family. We enjoy her company and we are so blessed to have her in our home.

---

3 sheets

3 sheets

2 sheets

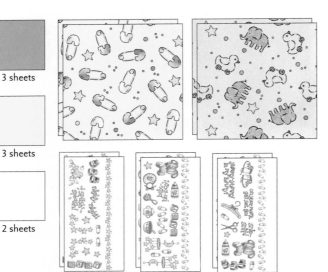

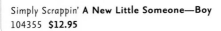

Simply Scrappin' **A New Little Someone—Boy**
104355 **$12.95**

BABY

boy-oh-boy!

Blake and Derek are sweet little brothers. They are kind and gentle with each other and love to be close to one another.
January 2004

---

3 sheets

3 sheets

2 sheets

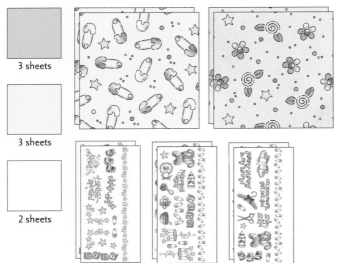

Simply Scrappin' **A New Little Someone—Girl**
104356 **$12.95**

proud grandparents

These pictures were taken the day we brought Amanda home from the hospital. Grandma and Grandpa H. were such a big help. I was happy because I got to sleep all afternoon and they were happy because they got to hold their new granddaughter all afternoon.
November 11, 2003

Patterned papers are shown as 50% swatches.

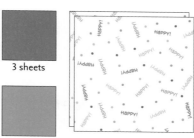
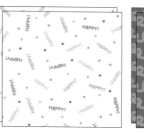
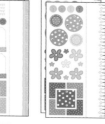
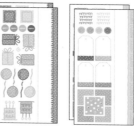

3 sheets

3 sheets

2 sheets

new! Simply Scrappin' **Polka Dot Party**
104366 **$12.95**

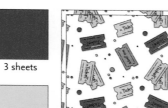
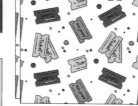
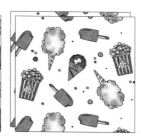

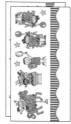
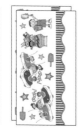

3 sheets

3 sheets

2 sheets

Simply Scrappin' **Time for Fun**
104361 **$12.95**

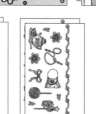
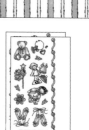

3 sheets

3 sheets

2 sheets

Simply Scrappin' **Buttons, Bows & Twinkletoes**
104357 **$12.95**

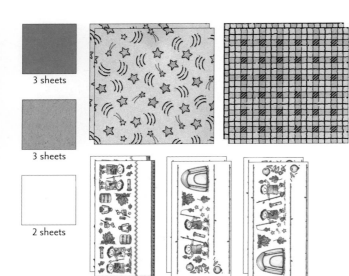

3 sheets

3 sheets

2 sheets

Simply Scrappin' **Campout**
104358 **$12.95**

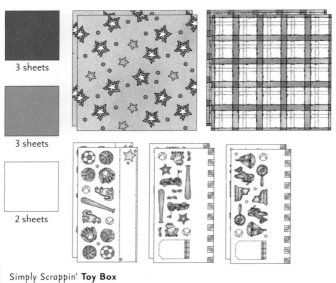

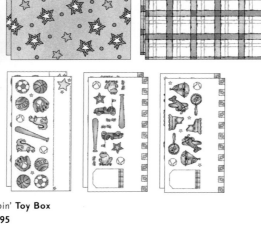

3 sheets

3 sheets

2 sheets

Simply Scrappin' **Toy Box**
104359 **$12.95**

3 sheets

3 sheets

2 sheets

new! Simply Scrappin' **Summer Sketches**
104365 **$12.95**

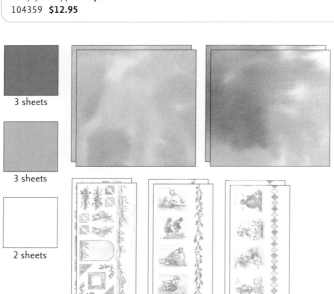

Patterned papers are shown as 50% swatches.

3 sheets

3 sheets

2 sheets

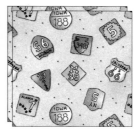

Simply Scrappin' **Travel Time**
104360 **$12.95**

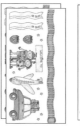

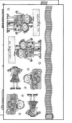

3 sheets

3 sheets

2 sheets

new! Simply Scrappin' **Vintage Keepsakes**
104363 **$12.95**

3 sheets

3 sheets

2 sheets

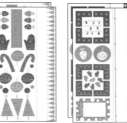

new! Simply Scrappin' **Sparkling Holiday**
104367 **$12.95**

DON'T MISS IT! Use magnetic sheets with our Everyday Flexible Phrases set, shown on page 195. Stamp and cut out each word for a great gift idea.

assorted paper products

a. Magnetic Sheets with Adhesive 8 x 10. 2 sheets per pkg.

101705	Magnetic Sheets with Adhesive	**$4.50**

b. Checkbook Covers Stamp and personalize for distinctive spending. Vinyl. 2 per pkg.

101958	Checkbook Covers	**$4.95**

c. Memo Cube 2-3/4 cube. Blank on 3 sides for stamping.

103062	Memo Cube	**$5.50**

d. Window Sheets 8-1/2 x 11. 3 sheets per pkg.

101249	Window Sheets	**$2.95**

e. Puzzles & Envelopes 5-1/2 x 4. 10 per pkg.

101824	Puzzles & Envelopes	**$5.50**

calendars

sm **f. Days-to-Remember Calendar** Give the gift of memories. Scrapbook pages you create enliven each month. The perforated pages become instant scrapbook pages. It's the ultimate personalized calendar! Acid free, lignin free, and buffered.

new! **6 x 6 Desktop Calendar**

104144	Ultrasmooth White	**$7.95**
104145	Confetti White	**$7.95**

8-1/2 x 11 Wall Calendar

102174	Ultrasmooth White	**$7.95**
102286	Confetti White	**$7.95**

12 x 12 Wall Calendar

103604	Ultrasmooth White	**$10.95**
103605	Confetti White	**$10.95**

g. Birthday Calendar Keep track of birthdays and other important occasions with these perpetual date trackers. Acid free, lignin free, and buffered. 5-1/2 x 14.

101398	Ultrasmooth White	**$7.95**
100559	Confetti White	**$7.95**

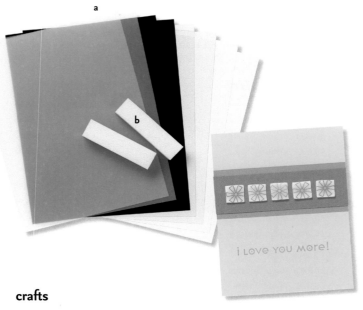

crafts

a. PolyShrink™ Make original jewelry, buttons, and charms. 8 x 10-1/2. 8 sheets per pkg. Assortment contains 2 sheets ea. of Black, Clear, Translucent, and White.

102937	White	$5.50
102583	Assortment	$5.50

b. Sanding Blocks The sanding block can be used for much more than preparing PolyShrink. Try rubbing it on our colored paper for an aged effect, or use it to sand a rough edge on your trimmed card stock. 2 per pkg.

103301	Sanding Blocks	$3.50

c. Premo Sculpey Kit Add unique dimension to your stamping project with this polymer clay that can be shaped, stamped, and baked. Comes with 3 tools to help shape and cut. Create ornaments, beads, pins, jewelry, or anything else you can imagine. 8 colors, 2 oz. ea. Black, Cadmium Red, Cadmium Yellow, Cobalt Blue, Gold, Green, Pearl, and White.

100244	Premo Sculpey Kit	$19.95

tags & more

d. Fun Frames & Tags Assortment 3-3/4 x 5. 12 oval frames and 12 tags, 12 rectangle frames and 12 tags. Acid free, lignin free, and buffered.

101104	Ultrasmooth White	$4.95
102980	Naturals Ivory	$4.95

e. Circle Tags 24 per package. 2-1/2 inch diameter.

102985	Glossy White	$2.95
103242	Confetti White	$2.95

f. Door Hangers & Tags 8 x 3-1/2. 18 door hangers and 18 tags.

102199	Glossy White	$5.50
100942	Confetti White	$5.50

g. Large Bookmarks 2-1/8 x 5-5/8. 25 per pkg.

102133	Ultrasmooth White	$4.50

h. Door Hanger Pouches 6-3/4 x 3-1/2. 12 per pkg.

102749	Ultrasmooth White	$3.95
102548	Naturals Ivory	$3.95

TRY THIS! The Sculpey Kit comes with 8 colors of clay, but you can mix them to create many other great colors! For instance, try mixing black and yellow—you'll end up with an olive-colored clay.

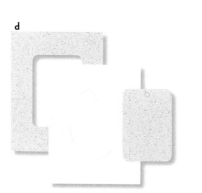

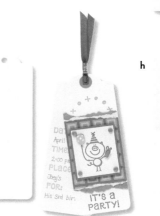

accessories

metal tags

a. Metal Edge Tags You'll love this fun accent for cards, pages, or other projects. Available in your choice of 3 metals with white card stock or white vellum. Choose circle or square tags. Each package contains six 2-inch tags and six 1-1/2-inch tags.

Aluminum

103372	White Squares	$3.95
103374	White Circles	$3.95
103371	Vellum Squares	$3.95
103373	Vellum Circles	$3.95

Brass

103888	White Squares	$4.95
103890	White Circles	$4.95
103887	Vellum Squares	$4.95
103889	Vellum Circles	$4.95

Copper

103892	White Squares	$4.95
103894	White Circles	$4.95
103891	Vellum Squares	$4.95
103893	Vellum Circles	$4.95

b. Metal Magic™ Stampers, crafters, and scrapbookers all love the look of metal and tags. Stampin' Up! combines these two trends into one terrific product. Metal Magic tags, available in 3 metals, include an impressive assortment of tags in a variety of shapes and sizes. The tags feature predrilled holes, which make it even easier to add eyelets, brads, or other embellishments. 12 tags, 6 square reinforcers, 8 circle reinforcers.

Stainless Steel

103659	Assortment I	$7.95
103660	Assortment II	$7.95

new! Brass

104085	Assortment I	$8.95
104086	Assortment II	$8.95

new! Copper

104083	Assortment I	$8.95
104084	Assortment II	$8.95

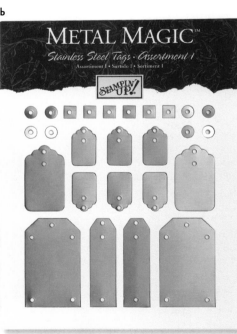

TRY THIS! You'll love the shine that our Metal Magic tags bring to your projects. See pages 154–155, 162–163, and 167 for color samples that demonstrate some of the possibilities.

tag and pennant sheets

a. Tag Sheets *sm* A versatile accent for pages, cards, and much more. 6 assortments to choose from based on our most popular color choices. Each assortment includes six 12 x 12 sheets of die-cut tags, 264 individual tags in all. Layer them or use them alone to add the perfect touch to your project. 6 sheets per pkg. Color packages include 1 of ea. color listed at bottom of page plus Confetti White and Confetti Tan. Confetti and Ultrasmooth packages contain 3 ea. of 2 colors. 12 x 12. **ⓐ ❶**

100214	Bold Brights	$6.95
100217	Earth Elements	$6.95
100215	Rich Regals	$6.95
100216	Soft Subtles	$6.95
100218	Confetti White & Tan	$6.95
100219	Ultrasmooth White & Vanilla	$6.95

b. Vellum Tag Sheets *sm* 8 sheets per pkg. 2 of ea. color listed at bottom of page. White package comes with 8 sheets of white only. 352 individual tags per pkg. **ⓐ ❶**

103583	Bold Brights	$8.95
103586	Earth Elements	$8.95
103585	Rich Regals	$8.95
103584	Soft Subtles	$8.95
103587	White	$8.95

c. Pennant Sheets *sm* These pennants are great for creating titles, journaling, and accents for scrapbook pages, cards, or other stamping projects. Each package contains more than 200 pennants in a variety of color choices and sizes, and the banner pieces are sized specifically to fit wide verse stamp sets, such as Phrase Starters II and Elegant Beginnings. Each package contains 210 flags, pennants, or photo corners per pkg. 6 sheets per pkg. Color packages include 1 of ea. color listed at bottom of page plus Confetti White and Confetti Tan. Confetti and Ultrasmooth packages contain 3 ea. of 2 colors. 12 x 12. **ⓐ ❶**

103588	Bold Brights	$6.95
103591	Earth Elements	$6.95
103590	Rich Regals	$6.95
103589	Soft Subtles	$6.95
103592	Confetti White & Tan	$6.95
103593	Ultrasmooth White & Vanilla	$6.95

die-cut box & tag sheets

You'll love these fun punch-out boxes in a selection of our 48 colors; colors listed at bottom of page. We've included tags, which make these boxes ready-made packaging for any special event. 6 sheets per pkg. Color packages include 1 of ea. color listed at bottom of page plus Confetti White and Confetti Tan. Confetti and Ultrasmooth packages contain 3 ea. of 2 colors. 12 x 12. **ⓐ ❶**

d. Party Favor Boxes & Tags

100226	Bold Brights	$6.95
100229	Earth Elements	$6.95
100227	Rich Regals	$6.95
100228	Soft Subtles	$6.95
100230	Confetti White & Tan	$6.95
new! 104201	Ultrasmooth Vanilla*	$6.95
new! 104202	Ultrasmooth White*	$6.95

*The Ultrasmooth assortment in our most popular box & tag sheet design, Party Favor, has been separated into two packages. Each pkg. includes 6 ea. of one color.

e. Trapezoid Boxes & Tags

100208	Bold Brights	$6.95
100211	Earth Elements	$6.95
100209	Rich Regals	$6.95
100210	Soft Subtles	$6.95
100212	Confetti White & Tan	$6.95
100213	Ultrasmooth White & Vanilla	$6.95

ⓐ = acid free   **❶** = lignin free   **ⓑ** = buffered

© 1990–2004 Stampin' Up!

a & b

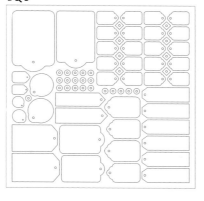

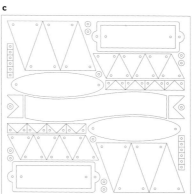

c

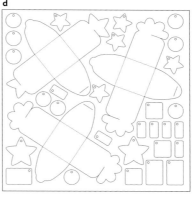

d

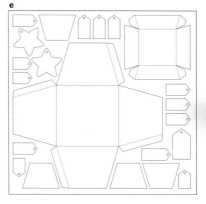

e

bold brights: Brilliant Blue, Glorious Green, Lovely Lilac, Real Red

rich regals: Baroque Burgundy, Ballet Blue, Night of Navy, Forest Foliage

earth elements: More Mustard, Old Olive, Creamy Caramel, Ruby Red

soft subtles: Barely Banana, Bliss Blue, Mellow Moss, Pretty in Pink

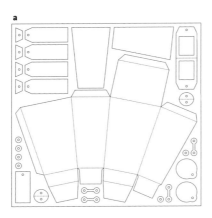

a

b

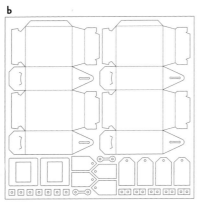

c

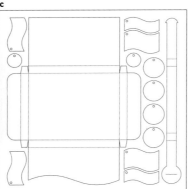

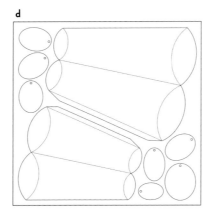

d

die-cut box & tag sheets

6 sheets per pkg. Color packages include 1 of ea. color listed at bottom of page plus Confetti White and Confetti Tan. Confetti and Ultrasmooth packages contain 3 ea. of 2 colors. 12 x 12. **a ❶**

new! a. Pillar Boxes & Tags

104316	Bold Brights	$6.95
104317	Earth Elements	$6.95
104318	Rich Regals	$6.95
104319	Soft Subtles	$6.95
104320	Confetti White & Tan	$6.95
104321	Ultrasmooth White & Vanilla	$6.95

new! b. Mini Gable Boxes & Tags

104322	Bold Brights	$6.95
104323	Earth Elements	$6.95
104324	Rich Regals	$6.95
104325	Soft Subtles	$6.95
104326	Confetti White & Tan	$6.95
104327	Ultrasmooth White & Vanilla	$6.95

c. Stationery Boxes & Tags

100202	Bold Brights	$6.95
100205	Earth Elements	$6.95
100203	Rich Regals	$6.95
100204	Soft Subtles	$6.95
100206	Confetti White & Tan	$6.95
100207	Ultrasmooth White & Vanilla	$6.95

d. Pouch Boxes & Tags

100220	Bold Brights	$6.95
100223	Earth Elements	$6.95
100221	Rich Regals	$6.95
100222	Soft Subtles	$6.95
100224	Confetti White & Tan	$6.95
100225	Ultrasmooth White & Vanilla	$6.95

die-cut box & tag sheets

Our exclusive die-cut box & tag sheets take the hassle out of creating patterns for a variety of projects. Just punch out, stamp, assemble, and embellish to create a unique gift package for any occasion. Use our Sticky Strip on page 224 to secure sides of the box. It's also easy to create your own custom box by cutting away part of the existing box. Try one style or try them all . . . it's all about creativity!

bold brights: Brilliant Blue, Glorious Green, Lovely Lilac, Real Red

rich regals: Baroque Burgundy, Ballet Blue, Night of Navy, Forest Foliage

earth elements: More Mustard, Old Olive, Creamy Caramel, Ruby Red

soft subtles: Barely Banana, Bliss Blue, Mellow Moss, Pretty in Pink

boxes & bags

a. Gable Boxes Small: 4-1/4 x 2-1/2 x 2-1/2; Medium: 6 x 4 x 4;
Large: 8 x 4-3/4 x 5-1/4; 6 per pkg.

101344	Small White	$4.50
102332	Small Kraft	$4.50
100906	Medium White	$5.95
102595	Medium Kraft	$5.95
101752	Large White	$6.95
100493	Large Kraft	$6.95

b. Gift Boxes Small: 2 x 2 x 2; Medium: 3 x 3 x 3; Large: 4 x 4 x 4. 3 per pkg.

102606	Small Kraft	$2.50
100483	Medium Kraft	$2.75
103157	Large Kraft	$2.95

c. Basket Box 3-3/8 x 5-7/8 x 1-3/4; 10 per pkg.

102997	Glossy White	$7.95

d. Lunch Bags 3-1/2 x 6 x 11. 25 per pkg.

100817	White	$3.95

e. Gift Sacks 4-3/4 x 8 x 10-1/2. 3 per pkg.

100900	White	$2.95
103321	Oatmeal	$2.95

f. Cellophane Bags Large Flat: 6 x 8; Medium Flat: 4 x 6; Small Flat: 3 x 5;
Large Gusset: 5 x 3 x 11-1/2; Medium Gusset: 4 x 2-1/2 x 9-1/2. 50 per pkg.

102210	Large Flat	$4.95
102757	Medium Flat	$4.50
103104	Small Flat	$3.95
101028	Large Gusset	$6.50
100664	Medium Gusset	$5.25

g. Organdy Bags Heat emboss these delicate bags for beautiful effects.
Use caution, as bags will melt with extreme heat. Large: 5-1/2 x 13-1/4;
Medium: 5-1/2 x 9; Small: 4-3/4 x 5-1/2; sizes are approximate. 3 per pkg.

102306	Large	$4.95
100993	Medium	$3.95
101623	Small	$2.95

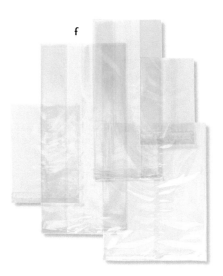

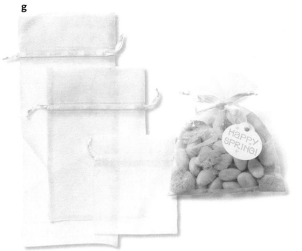

accessories

tool punches

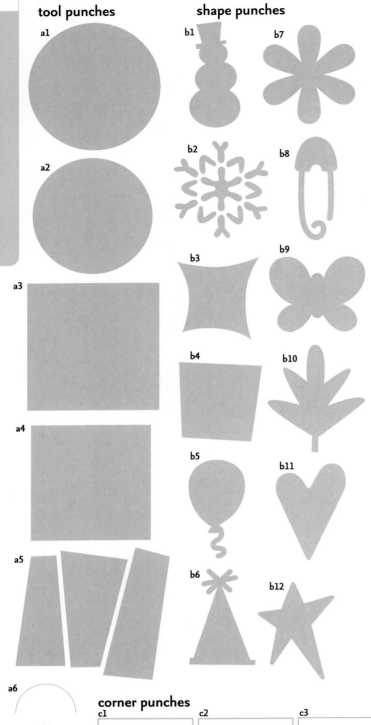

a1

a2

a3

a4

a5

a6

a7

a8

shape punches

b1

b2

b3

b4

b5

b6

b7

b8

b9

b10

b11

b12

corner punches

c1

c2

c3

corner pocket punches

d1

d2

corner slot punches

e1

e2

punches

You'll love the ease of our thumb punch—now available on our entire line of tool, shape, and corner punches. Our new large circle and square punches replace our AlphaAccents.

a. Tool Punches

new! a1	104401	1-3/8-inch Circle	$13.95
new! a2	104403	1-1/4-inch Circle	$13.95
a3	103375	1-3/8-inch Square	$13.95
new! a4	104400	1-1/4-inch Square	$13.95
new! a5	104406	Paper-Piecing *(available September 2004)*	$13.95
new! a6	104388	Slit *(available September 2004)*	$4.95
new! a7	104390	1/2-inch Circle	$4.95
new! a8	104389	Double Circle	$4.95

b. Shape Punches

new! b1	104397	Snowman	$9.95
new! b2	104398	Snowflake	$9.95
new! b3	104404	Concave Square	$9.95
new! b4	104405	Convex Square	$9.95
new! b5	104394	Balloon	$9.95
new! b6	104395	Party Hat	$9.95
new! b7	104392	Daisy	$9.95
new! b8	104396	Diaper Pin *(available September 2004)*	$9.95
new! b9	104393	Butterfly	$9.95
new! b10	104399	Leaf	$9.95
b11	103377	Folk Heart	$9.95
b12	103376	Folk Star	$9.95

c. Corner Punches

new! c1	104407	Notched	$10.95
c2	103379	Large Corner Rounder	$10.95
c3	103378	Small Corner Rounder	$5.95

d. Corner Pocket Punches

d1	103381	Square Steps	$10.95
new! d2	104408	Create-a-Corner	$10.95

e. Corner Slot Punches

new! e1	104391	Simplicity	$10.95
e2	103380	Wrought Iron	$10.95

f. Hand-Held Punches

f1	100392	1/4-inch Circle	$8.95
f2	100391	1/8-inch Circle	$8.95
f3	101227	1/16-inch Circle	$8.95
f4	102686	Rectangle	$8.95

hand-held punches

f1

f2

f3

f4

TRY THIS! To create a perfect mat with the Wrought Iron corner punch, cut the card stock 1/2-inch larger than the photo, then punch the four corners. With all other corner punches, cut the card stock 1/4-inch larger than the photo.

The Snowflake punch is a reverse punch, so you keep the card stock rather than the punched-out portion. Use the large circle or square punch to create a snowflake medallion.

storage

new! **a. Color Caddy™** New stamp pad storage as revolutionary as the pads it holds! Holds 48 Classic or Craft pads and 48 refills. Rotates for easy access. Some assembly required. Pads & refills not included.

104335   Color Caddy (Available September 2004)   **59.95**

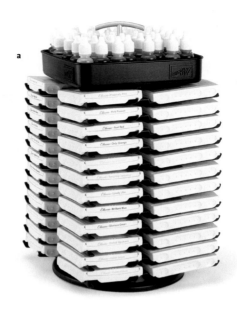

b. Stampin' Stack & Store Keep all your favorite craft goodies organized and at your fingertips with this complete storage system—or pick and choose the pieces that work best for you. Either way, you'll love being able to find eyelets, hemp twine, brads, or buttons in the blink of an eye. Complete system includes 1 Stampin' Stack, 4 Stampin' Store containers, and 4 Mini Stampin' Store containers.

You can also customize your own Stampin' Stack. It is designed to hold 6 eyelet or button containers or regular Stampin' Store containers (2-1/2 x 7/8) or 12 bead or Mini Stampin' Store containers (2-1/2 x 7/16).

103646   Stampin' Stack & Store   **$8.95**
103648   Stampin' Stack   **$5.95**
103649   Stampin' Store containers (6)   **$3.95**
103647   Mini Stampin' Store containers (6)   **$3.95**

new! **c. Craft Keepers** Safe storage for photos, papers, card stock, templates, and more. Snap closure. Expands to 1 inch thick. 3 per pkg.

104181   12 x 12 (actual size: 13 x 13)   **$7.95**
104182   8-1/2 x 11 (actual size: 9 x 11-1/2)   **$6.95**

d. Stampin' Carry™ Tuck essential stamping or scrapbook material in your Stampin' Carry and head off to your next stamp camp or crop without a worry. This strong but lightweight black bag, which also features the Stampin' Up! logo, makes packing what you need a cinch. You can fit a light table inside! Shoulder strap included. 13 x 13-1/2 x 3-1/2.

103578   Stampin' Carry   **$16.95**

e. Cropper Hopper™ Supply Tote This sturdy case provides a convenient way to carry all your favorite accessories. With tools on one side and stamps and paper on the other, stamping becomes a go-anywhere hobby. Manufactured exclusively for Stampin' Up! 11-1/2 x 9-1/2 x 3-3/4. (Product shown inside not included.)

103207   Cropper Hopper Supply Tote   **$14.95**

Stampin' Stack

Stampin' Store containers (6)

Mini Stampin' Store containers (6)

Stampin' Stack & Store (complete)
Beads and eyelets not included.

adhesives

a. 2-Way Glue Pen This adhesive is temporary when allowed to dry before adhering or permanent when adhered promptly. Acid free. 10 grams.

| 100425 | 2-Way Glue Pen | **$2.95** |

b. Liquid Glue Dual-tipped applicator lets you apply this clear, gel-like glue in thin lines or over wide areas. Acid free. 24 ml.

| 102620 | Liquid Glue | **$3.95** |

new! *sm* **c. SNAIL™ Adhesive** Try this **S**imple, **N**eat, **A**ffordable, **I**n **L**ine, double-stick adhesive; its convenient dispenser features a Stampin' Up! look of its own. This permanent multipurpose adhesive is a cost-effective choice. Acid free. 472 inches.

| 104332 | Permanent SNAIL Adhesive | **$6.95** |
| 104331 | Permanent SNAIL Refill (Refill not shown.) | **$4.25** |

d. Heat & Stick Powder This product lets you apply glitter or Pearl Ex to your entire stamped image with precision. Acid free. 1/2 oz.

| 100625 | Heat & Stick Powder | **$4.50** |

new! **e. Anywhere Glue Stick™** New rectangle shape allows you to access even the corners of your project. 2 per pkg. Acid free. 20 grams each.

| 104045 | Glue Sticks | **$3.95** |

new! **f. Sticky Strip** Use this double-sided, extra-tacky strip to adhere beads or make boxes stick tightly. Acid free. 1/4-inch wide. Approx. 10 yards.

| 104294 | Sticky Strip | **$6.95** |

g. Stampin' Dimensionals® 300 1/16-inch thick double-sided, adhesive foam dots. Acid free. Use multiple dimensionals for added height.

| 104430 | Stampin' Dimensionals | **$3.95** |

h. Glue Dots® Glue Dots are a super-sticky adhesive designed for use on three-dimensional accents used to embellish cards, scrapbook pages, and other projects. Glue Dots hold fast to paper, fabric, wood, foam, plastic, and more. This fast, clean adhesive is safe for kids too. No fumes, no mess, no drying time required. Acid free.

| 103683 | Mini Glue Dots (3/16-in. diameter, 250 dots.) | **$4.95** |
| *new!* 104183 | Pop-Up Glue Dots (1/2-in. diameter, 1/8-in. thick. 75 dots.) | **$3.95** |

sm **i. Memorabilia Pockets** Polypropylene, adhesive-backed assortment includes two 2 x 2, two 2 x 4-1/8, two 4 x 4-1/8, and one 5 x 4-15/16 pockets. Acid free.

| 103685 | Memorabilia Pockets | **$4.95** |

j. Adhesive Remover A quick, easy way to remove excess adhesive from unwanted areas, Adhesive Remover works like an eraser. Simply rub it on the sticky area, and that sticky problem will disappear. Note: It does not remove tape. 2 x 2.

| 103684 | Adhesive Remover | **$1.95** |

scissors & cutters

a. Cutting Mat This no-slip mat allows for safe cutting while protecting desks, tables, and countertops. Grid lines provide a guide for perfect cutting with your hobby blade every time. The self-healing mat means that no cut marks affect your next cut. 12 x 18.

| 101087 | Cutting Mat | **$14.95** |

b. Acrylic Graph & Grid Large, easy-to-read numbers in 2 directions eliminate the need to turn the ruler. The computer-generated grid ensures accurate and consistent cuts with your hobby blade. 6 x 12.

| 103158 | Acrylic Graph & Grid | **$9.95** |

c. Hobby Blade Extra sharp, with 5 refill blades. Comes in a convenient storage tube.

| 102449 | Hobby Blade & Refills | **$4.50** |

d. The Tearing Edge™ Create natural-looking torn edges with precision. Approx. 13 x 1-1/2.

| 102930 | The Tearing Edge | **$19.95** |

e. Coluzzle® Cutting System Starter set includes circle & oval template, cutting mat, and cutting knife in our 8-1/2 x 11 Craft Keeper. For creating perfect 1/8-inch mats or double mats, try our companion set, which includes slightly smaller circle and oval templates.

102264	Starter Set	**$19.95**
100489	Companion Set	**$11.95**
102721	Refill Blades (2)	**$3.95**

new! **f. Paper Cutter** Cuts paper up to 12 inches. New design features easy-to-read grid lines and black base. Measures widths up to 15-1/2. Rigid blade guide ensures straighter cut. Comes with 2 cutting blades. Refills include either a cutting and scoring blade or 2 cutting blades.

104152	Paper Cutter	**$24.95**
104154	Cutting & Scoring Blade Refills	**$4.95**
104153	Cutting Blade Refills	**$4.95**

g. Paper Snips Want to make a clean cut even around the corners and in tight places? These snips let you do exactly that. These small, thin-blade scissors provide expert cutting in even the tiniest of areas, and the precision-ground tips allow you to cut to the end of the blade. 2-1/2-inch blade length.

| 103579 | Paper Snips | **$9.95** |

h. Craft & Rubber Scissors These sharp, short-bladed scissors are great for multipurpose use and are especially suited for trimming your rubber stamps before assembling them. 1-3/4-inch blade length.

| 103179 | Craft & Rubber Scissors | **$19.95** |

i. Decorative Edge Scissors These large-handled scissors allow ease in cutting and come in 4 great patterns! 3-inch blade length.

102303	Colonial Charm	**$6.95**
101053	Deckle	**$6.95**
101130	Scallop	**$6.95**
100610	Wave	**$6.95**

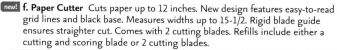

colonial charm

deckle

scallop

wave

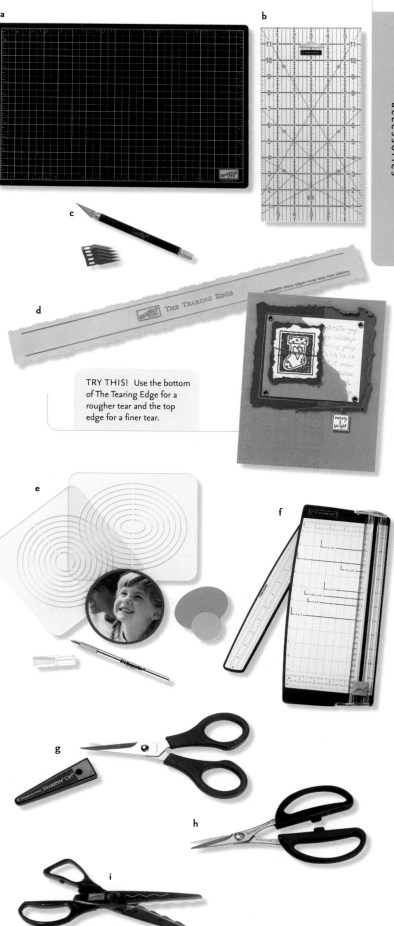

TRY THIS! Use the bottom of The Tearing Edge for a rougher tear and the top edge for a finer tear.

a

ink pads

blue frost

celebration

fiesta

late november

parfait

pumpkin patch

taffy

twist

a. Spectrum Pads These multicolor pads use the same acid-free dye inks as our Classic Stampin' Pads, so your Classic Stampin' Ink refills will re-ink both pads. (Specific colors used are listed on each Spectrum pad for easy refilling.) The innovative and easy-to-use pad design prevents the inks from bleeding during storage.

102694	Blue Frost	$11.95	102073	Parfait	$11.95
101492	Celebration	$11.95	101336	Pumpkin Patch	$11.95
101207	Fiesta	$11.95	103238	Taffy	$11.95
102367	Late November	$11.95	100926	Twist	$11.95

Create your own color combination with our Classic Ink Refills!

100000	Empty Spectrum Pad	$8.95

b. VersaMark Create a tone-on-tone design or a watermark effect with this unique pad and marker. Acid free. Refill: 1/2 oz.

102283	VersaMark Pad	$7.50
102193	VersaMark Pad Refill	$3.95
100901	VersaMarker™	$3.25

new! **c. Color Box® Petal Point® Chalk Pads** For a soft, rich look, choose these hybrid (dye and pigment) inks, which coordinate with a selection of our 48 colors. Fast drying and great for scrapbooking and direct-to-paper techniques. Refills are available in packs of 4. Each refill is 1/2 oz.

104277	Brights/Subtles Pad	$16.95
104278	Earths/Regals Pad	$16.95
104273	Brights Ink Refill	$14.95
104272	Earths Ink Refill	$14.95
104275	Regals Ink Refill	$14.95
104274	Subtles Ink Refill	$14.95

d. Top Boss® Tinted Embossing Pad Acid free. Refill: 1/2 oz.

101248	Top Boss Tinted Embossing Pad	$6.25
103137	Top Boss Tinted Embossing Ink Refill	$3.95

e. Encore!® Pads Add a rich, metallic look to your stamped projects with these acid-free, fade-resistant pigment ink pads. Metallic inks should be heat embossed when used in a scrapbook. These inks come in stackable, easy-to-hold pads. Refills: 1/2 oz.

101017	Gold	$8.95	101242	Gold Refill	$4.25
101039	Silver	$8.95	102124	Silver Refill	$4.25
new! 104280	Copper	$8.95	104281	Copper Refill	$4.25

f. StazOn™ Ink Pads This quick-drying, permanent ink works great on nonporous surfaces. Refills: 1/2 oz.

103359	Azure	$7.95	103356	Azure Ink Refill	$4.95
103000	Blazing Red	$7.95	101234	Blazing Red Ink Refill	$4.95
103360	Forest Green	$7.95	103357	Forest Green Ink Refill	$4.95
101406	Jet Black	$7.95	102566	Jet Black Ink Refill	$4.95
101987	Mustard	$7.95	102850	Mustard Ink Refill	$4.95
102079	Olive Green	$7.95	101438	Olive Green Ink Refill	$4.95
103358	Pumpkin	$7.95	103355	Pumpkin Ink Refill	$4.95
103353	Royal Purple	$7.95	103354	Royal Purple Ink Refill	$4.95
103088	Timber Brown	$7.95	100945	Timber Brown Ink Refill	$4.95
103146	Ultramarine	$7.95	102378	Ultramarine Ink Refill	$4.95

TRY THIS! Combine Spectrum pads and the brayer (see page 228) to create great background papers. When using the brayer, do not slide the colors together on the Spectrum pad.

b

c

d

e

brights/subtles

earths/regals

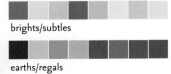

gold

silver

copper

f

azure

blazing red

forest green

jet black

mustard

olive green

pumpkin

royal purple

timber brown

ultramarine

DON'T MISS IT! Our full collection of Classic and Craft Stampin' Pads is shown on pages 200–203.

DON'T MISS IT! Our full collection of Stampin' Write markers and Stampin' Write journalers is shown on pages 201–203.

markers & pencils

a. Zig® Painty Double-tipped opaque pen.

| 102673 | Gold/Silver | **$5.95** |

b. Red Eye Rescue™ Marker Make all the red eyes in your photos disappear.

| 101126 | Red Eye Rescue Marker | **$3.95** |

new! c. Aqua Painter™ Use this versatile tool for controlled watercoloring and tearing mulberry paper. It's less messy and more transportable than a cup and watercolor brush. To use, fill reservoir with water. (1 medium and 1 large per pkg.)

| 103954 | Aqua Painter | **$16.95** |

d. Watercolor Brushes

100894	Flat	**$10.95**
101551	Medium	**$6.95**
101331	Small	**$5.95**

e. Blender Pens 2 brush tips on each. Use with Watercolor pencils and Stampin' Pastels to blend color. 3 per pkg. Acid free and xylene free.

| 102845 | Blender Pens | **$9.95** |

f. Metallic Art Pencils Add a rich shimmery luster to your stamped images. Convenient storage tube included. Acid free. 12 assorted colors.

| 101120 | Metallic Art Pencils | **$19.95** |

g. Pure Color Pencils Color goes on smooth. Color runs throughout the no-wood pencil, but it can be sharpened just like a regular pencil. Thin black coating can be scraped away. Acid free. 12 assorted colors.

| 100271 | Pure Color Pencils | **$19.95** |

h. Watercolor Pencils Made with deep pigments, our brilliantly colored pencils come in a sturdy tin container. Use alone to color stamped images or use with a blender pen, dampened watercolor brush, or Aqua Painter for lovely watercolor effects. Acid free. 24 assorted colors.

| 101879 | Watercolor Pencils | **$19.95** |

i. Pencil Sharpener Sharp steel blade gives a fine point every time. 2 sizes accommodate a range of pencils. Removable receptacle for shavings keeps things neat.

| 100745 | Pencil Sharpener | **$4.95** |

TRY THIS! Use our exclusive Watercolor pencils wet or dry to create a unique look. When they're dry they work like colored pencils and are great for coloring line images or sprucing up backgrounds. Color your image and blend the color with a dampened watercolor brush, blender pen, or Aqua Painter for a watercolor effect on any project. (For areas too tiny to color with the pencil, scribble a bit of color onto scratch paper and transfer to the tiny area in same manner as above.)

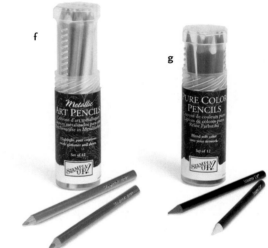

a

b

c

d

e

f

g

h

i

j

standard

jumbo

k

one-cell   two-cell   three-cell

essentials

a. Stampin' Scrub® Pad Get efficient, easy cleaning with this dual-sided tray containing replaceable black fiber scrubbing pads. Clean stamp on one side, blot dry on the other. Sized to fit even our largest stamps. Another Stampin' Up! exclusive! Each pad is approximately 7 x 5-3/4. Refill pads come in pkg. of 2.

102642	Stampin' Scrub	**$14.95**
101230	Stampin' Scrub Refill Pads	**$7.95**

b. Stampin' Mist® Stamp Cleaner Light rose-scented spray cleans and conditions your rubber stamps. 2 oz. Refill: 8 oz.

102394	Stampin' Mist	**$3.95**
101022	Stampin' Mist Refill	**$8.95**

c. Grid Paper Oversized pad of paper protects your stamping work surfaces. Serves as scratch paper and makes clean up a snap! Printed on one side with a grid and ruler for convenient measurements. 11 x 17. 100 sheets.

102787	Grid Paper	**$9.95**

d. Stamping Sponges 3 per pkg.

101610	Stamping Sponges	**$3.50**

e. Sponge Daubers 12 per pkg.

102892	Sponge Daubers	**$9.95**

f. Brayers For special-effects backgrounds and uniform inking on large stamps, nothing beats a brayer. Includes handle and soft rubber attachment. Acrylic and Foam snap-in attachments fit in the brayer handle shown and are sold separately.

102395	Handle with Rubber Attachment	**$11.50**
100430	Acrylic Attachment	**$7.50**
101052	Foam Attachment	**$6.95**

g. Bone Folder Use to score paper and make crisp folds.

102300	Bone Folder	**$6.50**

h. Crimper Crimps wire and paper up to 6-1/2 inches wide.

101618	Crimper	**$19.95**

i. Stamp-a-ma-jig™ Use this stamp positioner for fast and precise stamp alignment every time. Nonskid base. Includes reusable, wipe-clean imaging sheet for easy placement. (Stamp shown not included.)

	101049	Stamp-a-ma-jig	**$11.95**
new!	103953	Imaging Sheets Refill (3 per pkg.)	**$2.50**

j. Stampin' Around Handles Does not include cartridge. Ink cartridges are sold on pages 202–203. Embossing ink cartridges are sold on page 230.

102971	Stampin' Around Handle	**$3.95**
103661	Stampin' Around Jumbo Handle	**$5.95**

k. Stampin' Around Uninked Cartridges These cartridges come uninked, ready to create your own custom color combinations with any of our Classic ink refills.

103678	One-Cell Empty Jumbo Cartridge (not shown)	**$6.95**
101529	One-Cell Empty Cartridge	**$4.95**
102879	Two-Cell Empty Cartridge	**$4.95**
102576	Three-Cell Empty Cartridge	**$4.95**

stampin' kids

a. Stampin' Kids® Pads These recessed pads are designed with kids in mind. The ink is bright and washes off hands and out of most clothing (may require repeat washing). Pad surface is 1-7/8 x 2-3/4.

101577	Bear Brown	$2.95
100799	Beetle Black	$2.95
103203	Boxcar Blue	$2.95
101887	Gumball Green	$2.95
102453	Poppin' Purple	$2.95
101897	Princess Pink	$2.95
101177	Robin Red	$2.95
102588	Yahoo Yellow	$2.95

a

- bear brown
- beetle black
- boxcar blue
- gumball green
- poppin' purple
- princess pink
- robin red
- yahoo yellow

b. Stampin' Kids Markers Fun and economical way to introduce kids to the fun of paper arts. As with any child's art project, cover child's clothing for protection. 20 assorted colors.

102328	Stampin' Kids Markers	$4.95

b

c

c. Art Pencils Add color to your stamped art with our Art pencils. The assortment features the Stampin' Up! logo and offers a number of coloring options. Acid free. 12 per pkg.

101092	Art Pencils	$6.95

d. Tattoo Kits Kids of all ages love our Tattoo Kits! FD&C-approved inks fade and wash off within a day approximately. Nontoxic. Stamp images below are shown actual size.

Tattoo Kit I Contents: Navy pad, 6 markers (Black, Blue, Green, Henna, Red, Yellow), and 6 stamps in a vinyl pouch.

100388	Tattoo Kit I	$13.95
101562	Navy Tattoo Ink Refill (1/2 oz.)	$3.95

Tattoo Kit II Contents: Black pad, 6 markers (Blue, Green, Orange, Pink, Purple, Red), and 6 stamps in a vinyl pouch.

100389	Tattoo Kit II	$13.95
101982	Black Tattoo Ink Refill (1/2 oz.)	$3.95

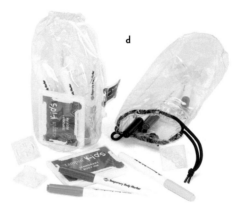

d

e

e. Tattoo Markers Dries quickly; washes off easily. FD&C-approved. 6 per pkg. (Black, Blue, Green, Orange, Pink, Purple)

100390	Tattoo Markers	$6.95

tattoo kit I

tattoo kit II

heat embossing

a. Heat Tool Use this electric heat tool with embossing powders and to heat-set pigment inks.

100005	Heat Tool	**$26.95**

b. Powder Pals Keep your work area neat and save glitters and powders with this terrific tool. Comes with 2 trays and a brush for clean up.

102197	Powder Pals	**$19.95**

c. Embossing Buddy Rub across paper to reduce static.

103083	Embossing Buddy	**$4.50**

d. Embossing Kit Contents: 1/2 oz. Sterling Silver Stampin' Emboss® Powder, 1/2 oz. Gold Glory Stampin' Emboss® Powder, Mini Top Boss® Tinted Embossing Pad, 1/2 oz. Top Boss® Tinted Embossing Refill, and instructions for use.

103280	Embossing Kit	**$14.95**

e. Stampin' Emboss Powder Add dimension and impact to any image. Try it on your next masterpiece! Acid free.

102440	Black (1 oz.)	**$4.50**
100442	Classy Copper (1 oz.)	**$4.50**
101058	Crystal Clear (1 oz.)	**$4.50**
100837	Gold Glory (1 oz.)	**$4.50**
103151	Hologram Highlights (1/2 oz.)	**$4.50**
101930	Iridescent Ice (1/2 oz.)	**$4.50**
103273	Sterling Silver (1 oz.)	**$4.50**
100526	Vintage Verdigris (1 oz.)	**$4.50**
100551	Winter White (1 oz.)	**$4.50**
100477	Glassy Glaze Enamel (1 oz.)	**$4.50**

f. Detail Embossing Powder This powder preserves the fine detail in your stamped images. 1/2 oz.

101040	Black	**$4.50**
101428	Clear	**$4.50**
103342	Gold	**$4.50**
101781	Silver	**$4.50**
100963	White	**$4.50**

g. Embossing Stacks With stacks, it's easy to coordinate colors. 4 stacks available with 1/2 oz. of 4 colors listed at left.

100091	Brights	**$16.95**
100089	Earths	**$16.95**
100090	Regals	**$16.95**
100088	Subtles	**$16.95**

h. Stampin' Around Embossing Ink Cartridges Not pictured. Acid free. Refill: 1/2 oz.

new!	104432	Clear Embossing Cartridge & Ink Refill	**$9.95**
	102391	Clear Embossing Ink Refill	**$3.95**

black
opaque and bold

classy copper
copper with a rich shine

crystal clear
smooth-flowing, clear powder to be used over colored ink, allowing the color to show through

gold glory
gold metallic with a foil-like shine

hologram highlights
crystal clear base with hologram glitter for a reflective flashy shine

iridescent ice
crystal clear base with iridescent glitter for stunning sparkle

sterling silver
silver metallic with a foil-like shine

vintage verdigris
green with copper patina

winter white
crisp, opaque white

glassy glaze enamel
ultrathick, clear powder for incredible stained-glass effects

black

clear

gold

silver

white

brights
red, green, orange, pink

earths
mustard, olive, rust, dark brown

regals
burgundy, forest green, blue, navy

subtles
light blue, light pink, lavender, sage

HELLO!

DON'T MISS IT! We recommend the VersaMark or Top Boss embossing pads (sold on page 226) for your embossing projects. The ingredients in these pads make them the best choice.

dry embossing

All Classy Brass templates feature exclusive designs. Many coordinate with popular Stampin' Up! stamp sets. Most templates also feature a decorative edge for embossed borders. For the custom look of elegant embossed images, collect all of these beautiful designs.

102986	All-Around Alphabet	$14.95
new! 104293	Bloomin' Wonderful	$14.95
100399	Bold Basics	$14.95
102273	Bold Greetings	$14.95
103341	Border Builders	$19.95
100496	Daisy	$14.95
100403	Delightful Doodles	$9.95
103603	Everyday Edges	$19.95
101665	Frames & Borders	$14.95
100842	Fresh Flowers	$14.95
100402	Love without End	$14.95
new! 104291	Polka Dot Party	$14.95
new! 104290	Simple Seasons	$9.95
100401	Simply Spring	$14.95
new! 104292	Shapes	$14.95
100400	Snowflakes	$14.95
102270	Special Occasion	$14.95
101963	Squares & Minis	$9.95

a. Light Table Embossing has never been easier. Our light table features a stainless steel frame, thick plexi-glass top, tilt-up device, and bright, even light. This gives you the perfect surface for use with our Classy Brass templates. 10 x 12 work area.

102888	Light Table	$49.95

b. Stylus Use small tip for lightweight papers and large tip for card stock.

100663	Stylus	$2.50

c. Empressor™ Stylus Dual-tipped, roller-ball embossing tool features new comfort grips and works with any template. Smooth-rolling action reduces paper tearing. Small tip is perfect for small patterns and lightweight papers; large tip works great on card stock.

100716	Empressor Stylus	$10.95

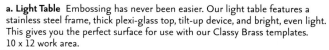
all-around alphabet

bloomin' wonderful

c

bold basics

bold greetings

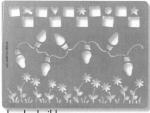
border builders

daisy

delightful doodles

everyday edges

frames & borders

fresh flowers

love without end

polka dot party

simple seasons

simply spring

TRY THIS! When dry embossing, rub waxed paper over the surface to be embossed. This allows the stylus to move easily over the card stock.

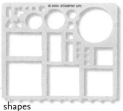
shapes

snowflakes

special occasion

squares & minis

stampin' glitter®

a. Stampin' Glitter A spot of shimmer transforms your creations. Apply with Heat & Stick powder, Liquid Glue, or a 2-Way Glue Pen, sold separately. 1/2 oz.

102023	Dazzling Diamonds	**$4.50**
103351	Gold Glitz	**$4.50**
103350	Green Glimmer	**$4.50**
103352	Romantic Red	**$4.50**
103349	Silver Shine	**$4.50**

TRY THIS! Heat & Stick Powder is an excellent product for adhering glitter and Pearl Ex to your stamped image. See page 224 for ordering information.

pearl ex powders

b. Pearl Ex Achieve fabulous effects from a smooth, pearly luster to a highly metallic sheen with these versatile iridescent powders! Mix with Lumiere® liquid medium to apply as a paint, or apply dry with a watercolor or stipple brush or sponge. Mix with embossing powder for shimmery embossing. 3 grams per bottle.

new!	104299	Assortment I	**$11.95**
new!	104300	Assortment II	**$11.95**
new!	104301	Assortment III	**$11.95**
	101319	Lumiere (2.25 fl. oz.)	**$5.95**

c. Stipple Brushes No. 2 and No. 4. 2 per pkg.

101399	Stipple Brushes	**$6.95**

d. Crystal Effects Add a dimensional, lacquered look to any stamped image. Acid free. 2 oz.

101055	Crystal Effects	**$6.25**

a

dazzling diamonds | gold glitz | green glimmer | romantic red | silver shine

b

lumiere

assortment I

silver | super bronze | duo green/ yellow | interference blue | interference red | turquoise

assortment II

aztec gold | micro pearl | spring green | super russet | interference violet | true blue

assortment III

interference gold | flamingo pink | duo blue/ green | super copper | duo red/ blue | misty lavender

The top swatch represents each color applied to black paper, and the bottom swatch is applied to white paper.

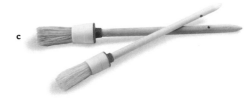

c

d

TRY THIS! Add a layer of shine to your stamped images with Crystal Effects. For a semiglossy effect, brush it over the entire surface of your card stock or paper with a watercolor brush.

eyelets

Embellish your projects with the hottest accessory around! Colors coordinate with many of our 48 colors. Eyelet tools sold separately. Single color eyelets include approx. 200 of each. Assortments include approx. 50 each of 4 colors.

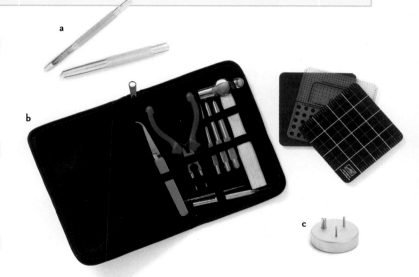

small circles

			Colors	Price
100370	Black			$5.95
100374	Gold			$5.95
100372	Real Red			$5.95
100373	Silver			$5.95
100371	White			$5.95
100377	Basic		Black, White, Gold, Silver	$5.95
100375	Bold Brights I		Brilliant Blue, Glorious Green, Real Red, Yoyo Yellow	$5.95
100376	Bold Brights II		Green Galore, Lovely Lilac, Only Orange, Positively Pink	$5.95
100381	Earth Elements		Creamy Caramel, More Mustard, Old Olive, Really Rust	$5.95
100380	Rich Regals		Baroque Burgundy, Bordering Blue, Forest Foliage, Night of Navy	$5.95
100378	Soft Subtles I		Barely Banana, Mellow Moss, Perfect Plum, Pretty in Pink	$5.95
100379	Soft Subtles II		Bliss Blue, Blush Blossom, Lavender Lace, Sage Shadow	$5.95

shapes

			Colors	Price
100369	Small Flowers		Barely Banana, Lavender Lace, Pretty in Pink, White	$9.95
100364	Squares		Brocade Blue, Close to Cocoa, More Mustard, Ruby Red	$9.95
100362	Stars		Brilliant Blue, Real Red, Silver, Summer Sun	$9.95
100363	Triangles		Green Galore, Only Orange, Silver, Tempting Turquoise	$9.95
100367	Large Circles		White, Silver, Real Red, Black	$9.95
100365	Large Ovals		Baroque Burgundy, Old Olive, Perfect Plum, Vanilla	$9.95
100366	Large Hearts		Pink Passion, Pretty in Pink, Real Red, White	$9.95
100368	Large Flowers		Lovely Lilac, Positively Pink, Real Red, Yoyo Yellow	$9.95

a. Eyelet Tool Kit Includes 1/8-inch anywhere punch and universal eyelet setter.

101016   Eyelet Tool Kit   **$7.95**

new! b. Crafters' Tool Kit Includes 3/16- and 1/8-inch anywhere punches, universal eyelet setter, small- and large-eye needles, paper-piercing tool, bottle-nosed pliers with wire cutter, cross-lock tweezers, and hammer. Also includes paper-piercing pad, paper-piercing template, and setting mat, each 4 x 4. Instructions included. All packaged in a durable, nylon zip case with outside pocket. Everything you need for wire and paper crafting.

104310   Crafters' Tool Kit   **$39.95**

c. Paper Popper™ What can you do when card stock and paper build up in your anywhere punch? Use the Paper Popper! Place the anywhere punch on the corresponding metal dowel and lightly tap the punch with a hammer to loosen the paper inside. This is a must-have accessory for every eyelet user! For best results, clean punch frequently.

103650   Paper Popper   **$7.95**

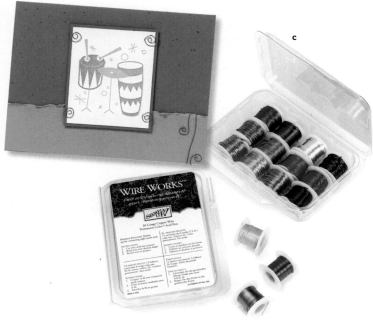

embellishments

a. Skeleton Leaves Apply directly to projects or use as stencils with a foam brayer. All natural; colors and shapes may vary. 10 per pkg.

102750	Skeleton Leaves	$3.95

new! **b. Brads** Wonderful for embellishing and layering. Can be embossed to create a variety of colors! Use a 1/16-inch Circle punch to make holes for these tiny fasteners. Approx. 200 per container.

104337	Gold	$6.95
104336	Silver	$6.95

c. Wire Works Wonderful wire for whimsical accents! Available in 2 weights: choose 22-gauge for a slightly thicker and heavier wire and 26-gauge for a thinner, more flexible wire. Acid free.

12 colors. Dark Blue, Forest, Green, Gold, Lemon, Magenta, Purple, Plum, Red, Seafoam Green, Silver, Tangerine. Approx. 8 yards per spool.

102808	26-Gauge	$19.95

12 colors. Christmas Green, Dark Blue, Green, Lemon, Magenta, Natural, Peacock Blue, Peach, Purple, Red, Silver, Tangerine. Approx. 6 yards per spool.

101833	22-Gauge	$19.95

new! **d. Beads** Beads add an appealing accent to any project. Micro beads are clear without holes. Approx. .8 mm. Colored beads are a mix of glass seed and glass bugle beads. Approximately 30 grams per container.

104271	Neutrals	$4.95
104270	Brights	$4.95
104269	Earths	$4.95
104268	Regals	$4.95
104267	Subtles	$4.95
104266	Micro	$4.95

new! **e. Buttons** Use on cards, scrapbook pages, tags, or any other stamping project. Buttons add dimension and interest to any creation and work wonderfully when used alongside other accents, such as hemp twine, linen thread, Wire Works, or ribbon. Hand-dyed to coordinate with a selection of our 48 colors; available colors listed below. Approx. 80 square and circle buttons in 2 sizes.

103981	Neutrals (Basic Black, Close to Cocoa, Creamy Caramel, Vanilla)	$6.95
103977	Bold Brights (Brilliant Blue, Green Galore, Lovely Lilac, Real Red)	$6.95
103978	Earth Elements (More Mustard, Old Olive, Really Rust, Ruby Red)	$6.95
103979	Rich Regals (Ballet Blue, Baroque Burgundy, Forest Foliage, Night of Navy)	$6.95
103980	Soft Subtles (Bliss Blue, Mellow Moss, Pale Plum, Pretty in Pink)	$6.95

I hope your birthday is, like, totally cool!

fibers

a. Hemp Twine Approx. 12 yards. Listed in the order shown. **$2.50**

101259	Black	100982	Natural
101080	Green	102875	Red
102859	Purple	101509	Blue
101949	Gold		

new! b. Linen Thread Sewing on cards and scrapbook pages is all the rage. Use this linen thread for all your creative projects. Diameter is fine enough for use with buttons or with needles from our Crafters' Tool Kit. 15 yds.

104199	Linen Thread	**$4.50**

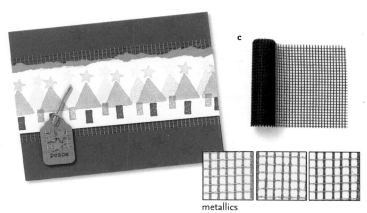
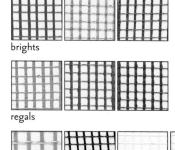
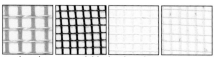
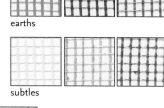

c. Magic Mesh This self-adhesive accent works great on cards, pages, gifts, and tags. Just unroll it and place it anywhere you want. With 19 colors, you're bound to find one to complement your project. And if these colors aren't enough, use any of our wonderful ink pads and the foam brayer to create custom-colored mesh! And don't stop there. Weave wire, ribbon, or hemp twine through the mesh for added variety. Approx. 2-1/2-inch wide. 1 yard. Mesh colors may vary depending on dye lots.

new!	104195	Metallics	**$12.95**
new!	104197	Brights	**$12.95**
new!	104196	Earths	**$12.95**
new!	104194	Regals	**$12.95**
new!	104193	Subtles	**$12.95**
new!	104198	Linen	**$4.50**
	103682	Black	**$4.50**
	103680	White	**$4.50**
	103681	Natural	**$4.50**

metallics

brights

earths

regals

subtles

single colors: natural, black, white, linen

d. Fancy Fibers™ You'll love our fibers, which coordinate with our 48 colors. Add dimension to your cards, tags, and layouts. Make quick borders, frames, or accents. Available in 5 different coordinating packages; assortment may vary. 6 colors on a card. Approx. 2 yards of ea. color, approx. 12 yards total. Please purchase sufficient fibers to complete your projects.

100395	Brights	**$6.95**
100396	Earths	**$6.95**
100393	Regals	**$6.95**
100394	Subtles	**$6.95**
100397	Neutrals	**$6.95**

brights   earths   regals   subtles   neutrals

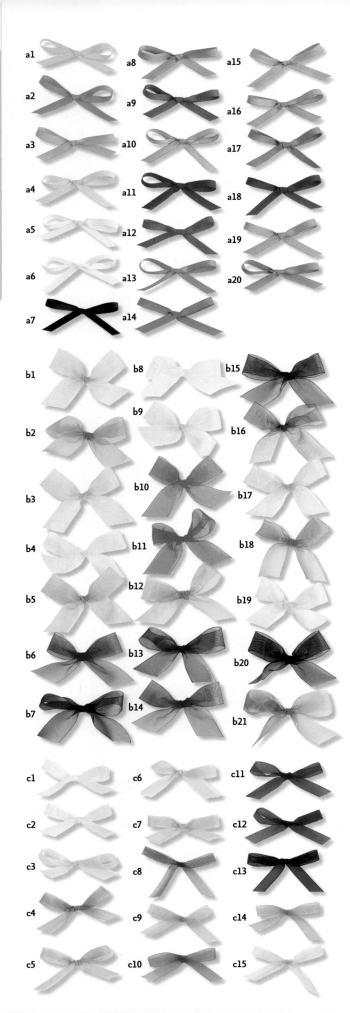

ribbon

a. Grosgrain Ribbon 1/4-inch wide; approx. 25 yards.   **$5.95**

a1	101926	Light Pink		a11	102718	Cranberry
a2	103064	Tangerine		a12	102682	Red
a3	102684	Yellow Gold		a13	101569	Rose
a4	101298	Maize		a14	100001	Kelly Green
a5	100455	Cream		a15	101637	Apple Green
a6	102819	White		a16	103114	Spring Moss
a7	102712	Black		a17	101156	Taupe
a8	100538	Bluebird		a18	100847	Royal
a9	103113	Delphinium		a19	102119	Turquoise
a10	101666	Light Orchid		a20	102950	French Blue

b. 7/8-inch Organdy Ribbon Approx. 25 yards.   **$6.25**

b1	103270	Silver		b11	101224	Red
b2	103107	Gold		b12	101597	Lavender
b3	102650	Maize		b13	100936	Purple
b4	100525	Ivory		b14	101204	Royal Blue
b5	101454	Mauve		b15	101854	Hunter Green
b6	100437	Burgundy		b16	102388	Olive Green
b7	103283	Navy		b17	102153	Celery
b8	102978	White		b18	101547	Kelly Green
b9	102735	Light Pink		b19	103163	Light Blue
b10	103046	Bright Pink		b20	103315	Black

b21	101441	Rainbow	**$8.95**

c. 3/8-inch Organdy Ribbon Approx. 25 yards.   **$4.95**

c1	101613	White	new! c9	104259	Celery
c2	100589	Ivory	new! c10	104258	Olive
c3	103019	Light Pink	new! c11	104260	Wine
c4	101644	Orchid	new! c12	104256	Navy
c5	102217	Blue	new! c13	104254	Black
c6	100807	Light Blue	new! c14	104257	Gold
c7	102758	Light Green	new! c15	104253	Silver
new! c8	104255	Green		

new! d. Cord   **$5.95**

This new cord is finer and more delicate than before! Approx. 75 yds.

d1	104303	Gold
d2	104304	Silver
d3	104302	Copper

d1    d2   d3

TRY THIS! Ribbon adds appeal to your stamped projects. Try these ideas:
- Stamp a personalized message on it with the Everyday Flexible Phrases set on page 195.
- Create ribbon in any color by applying ink to white ribbon with the brayer shown on page 228.
- The Double Circle punch on page 222 provides holes for perfect placement. Simply punch, thread the ribbon through the holes, and tie a bow.

stamp index

[COVER A] In Full Bloom, Simple Type, and Classic Alphabet sets; Bloomin' wheel; Creamy Caramel and Naturals Ivory card stock; White vellum tag sheets; Rich Regals Pillar boxes & tags; Copper Kiss Designer Series vellum; Chocolate Chip, Basic Brown, Close to Cocoa, Sage Shadow, and Baroque Burgundy Classic pads; VersaMark pad; Baroque Burgundy cartridge; watercolor brush; Classy Copper embossing powder; Taupe grosgrain ribbon; brads; 1/16" Circle punch; Stampin' Dimensionals

[COVER B] Bold Butterfly, Alphadots, Simple Type Alphabet, and Simple Type Numbers sets; Whirly-Twirly wheel; Sage Shadow, Rose Red, and Ultrasmooth Vanilla card stock; Ultrasmooth tag sheets; Rose Red, Sage Shadow, Creamy Caramel, and Chocolate Chip Craft pads; Rose Red cartridge; VersaMark pad; Earth Elements, Soft Subtles II, and Rich Regals eyelets; Stampin' Dimensionals; linen thread; sewing machine and thread; water squirt bottle

[COVER C] Summer by the Sea and Wonderful Words sets; Rose Red, Chocolate Chip, Naturals Ivory, White vellum, and Sage Shadow card stock; Basic Brown, Chocolate Chip, Sage Shadow, Rose Red, and Blush Blossom Classic pads; Chocolate Chip Craft pad; watercolor brush; linen thread; Silver brads; Stampin' Dimensionals; large needle

[COVER D] All the Best set; Baroque Burgundy, Naturals Ivory, Rose Red, Chocolate Chip, Sage Shadow, and Creamy Caramel card stock; Creamy Caramel Classic pad; Sage Shadow, Chocolate Chip, and Rose Red markers; linen thread; Paper-Piecing punch; Stampin' Dimensionals; large needle

[2-3] Shapes & Shadows, Pure & Simple Alphabet Upper, Newsprint Alphabet, Classic Alphabet, and Classic Numbers sets; Sage Shadow, Ultrasmooth Vanilla, Chocolate Chip, and Creamy Caramel card stock; Chocolate Chip, Sage Shadow, and Creamy Caramel Craft pads; VersaMark pad; Silver brads; Classy Copper embossing powder; Stampin' Dimensionals; watercolor brush; stamping sponges; 1/2" and 1/8" Circle punches; paper crimper; linen thread; Natural hemp twine; Square Copper Metal Edge tags

[2-3 B] Shapes & Shadows and Sassy Sayings II sets; Naturals Ivory, Chocolate Chip, Creamy Caramel, Rose Red, and Ultrasmooth Vanilla card stock; Chocolate Chip, Creamy Caramel, and Rose Red Classic pads; VersaMark pad; Vellum Circle Copper Metal Edge tags; Stampin' Dimensionals; paper crimper; 26-gauge Wire Works; Earths beads; Silver brads; Classy Copper embossing powder; linen thread

[2-3 C] Shapes & Shadows and Alphadots sets; Ultrasmooth Vanilla and Naturals Ivory card stock; Sage Shadow, Rose Red, Baroque Burgundy, and Chocolate Chip Craft pads; Rose grosgrain ribbon; Stampin' Dimensionals; Bold Brights II eyelets; linen thread

[2-3 D] Shapes & Shadows, All-Year Cheer II, and Simple Type Alphabet sets; Chocolate Chip, Naturals Ivory, Sage Shadow, Creamy Caramel, and Rose Red card stock; Chocolate Chip, Rose Red, Creamy Caramel, and Sage Shadow Craft pads; Stampin' Dimensionals; 1/16" Circle punch; linen thread; needle

[2-3 E] Shapes & Shadows and Season's Greetings sets; Baroque Burgundy, Creamy Caramel, Chocolate Chip, Sage Shadow, and Ultrasmooth Vanilla card stock; Ultrasmooth tag sheets; Baroque Burgundy, Sage Shadow, and Close to Cocoa Classic pads; Stampin' Dimensionals; Cream grosgrain ribbon; linen thread; Ivory 7/8" organdy ribbon; Natural hemp twine; watercolor brush; sewing machine and thread

[2-3 F] Shapes & Shadows set; By Definition background stamp; Naturals Ivory, Creamy Caramel, Sage Shadow, Chocolate Chip, and Rose Red card stock; Close to Cocoa, Rose Red, Baroque Burgundy, Creamy Caramel, Chocolate Chip, and Sage Shadow Craft pads; stamping sponges; 1/8" Circle punch; linen thread; Stampin' Dimensionals; watercolor brush; Rich Regals eyelets; Earths beads; sewing machine and thread

[4 A] Let's Party and Sassy Sayings II sets; Night of Navy, Ultrasmooth White, and Old Olive card stock; Pickles Designer Series paper; Old Olive, Night of Navy, and White Craft pads; Large Circle eyelets; Earths Fancy Fibers

[4 B] Spring Fling, Classic Alphabet, and Alphadots sets; Old Olive, Night of Navy, and Ultrasmooth White card stock; Old Olive, White, and Night of Navy Craft pads; Basic Black journaler; Stampin' Dimensionals; White Magic Mesh; Pickles Designer Series paper; White Square Aluminum Metal Edge tags; Oval eyelets; Earth Elements buttons

[4 C] Holiday Basics and All-Year Cheer I sets; Dots & Checks background stamp; White vellum card stock; Rich Regals pennant sheets; Earth Elements Pouch boxes & tags; Ultrasmooth tag sheets; White and Old Olive Craft pads; Night of Navy Classic pad; watercolor brush; Star eyelets; 1/16" Circle punch; Silver cord; Stampin' Dimensionals; crochet thread

[5 A] Simple Sayings II, All-Year Cheer, and Buds & Blossoms sets; Bold Blooms wheel; Ultrasmooth White and Orchid Opulence card stock; Soft Subtles mulberry paper; Ultrasmooth tag sheets; Sweet Designer Series paper; Basic Black Classic pad; Orchid Opulence Craft pad; Orchid Opulence ink refill; empty jumbo cartridge; sanding blocks; Light Orchid grosgrain ribbon; Stampin' Dimensionals; Small Flower eyelets; crochet thread

[5 B] Buds & Blossoms, Classic Alphabet, and Classic Numbers sets; Bold Blooms wheel; Gable Green, Green Galore, Orchid Opulence, and Tempting Turquoise card stock; Ultrasmooth tag sheets; Sweet Designer Series paper; Green Galore, Orchid Opulence, Tempting Turquoise, and Yoyo Yellow Craft pads; Tempting Turquoise ink refill; empty jumbo cartridge; VersaMark pad; Stampin' Pastels; Stainless Steel Metal Magic tags; Bold Brights II eyelets; Stampin' Dimensionals; 1/16" Circle punch; Light Orchid, Turquoise, and Apple Green grosgrain ribbon; crochet thread

[5 C] Buds & Blossom and All-Year Cheer III sets; Delicate Design wheel; Tempting Turquoise, Ultrasmooth White, and Orchid Opulence card stock; Sweet Designer Series paper; Tempting Turquoise Classic pad; Tempting Turquoise cartridge; Bold Brights II eyelets; Purple hemp twine; Stampin' Dimensionals; Vellum Circle Aluminum Metal Edge tags; crochet thread

[6 A] Love without End, Classic Alphabet, Alphadots Numbers, Newsprint Numbers, and Alphadots sets; Yoyo Yellow, Only Orange, Green Galore, Pink Passion, and Ultrasmooth White card stock; Yoyo Yellow, Only Orange, Pink Passion, Green Galore, and Yoyo Yellow Craft pads; Basic Black journaler; Bold Brights I eyelets; Large Flower eyelets; Stampin' Dimensionals; watercolor brush; Maize grosgrain ribbon; crochet thread

[6 B] Stardust and Classic Alphabet sets; Creamy Caramel, Basic Black, More Mustard, Ruby Red, and Confetti Cream card stock; More Mustard, Basic Black, Chocolate Chip, and Ruby Red Craft pads; Creamy Caramel and Ruby Red Classic pads; Basic Black marker; stamping sponges; Gold brads; Gold 3/8" organdy ribbon; Earths Fancy Fibers; Brass Metal Magic tags; White Circle Brass Metal Edge tags; linen thread

[7 A] Stipple Celebrations and Classic Alphabet sets; Busy Blocks wheel; Confetti White, White vellum, and Baroque Burgundy card stock; Rich Regals Pillar boxes & tags; Not Quite Navy, Forest Foliage, Ballet Blue, and Baroque Burgundy Craft pads; Ballet Blue jumbo cartridge; Rich Regals eyelets; Silver cord; watercolor brush; Stampin' Dimensionals; Bluebird Grosgrain ribbon

[7 B] Welcome, Little One set; Mellow Moss and Ultrasmooth White card stock; Soft Subtles tag sheets; Slumber Party Designer Series vellum; Basic Black, Pretty in Pink, Barely Banana, Mellow Moss, and Blush Blossom Classic pads; Subtles Fancy Fibers; watercolor brush; Soft Subtles buttons; Light Pink 3/8" organdy ribbon; Stampin' Dimensionals; needle and thread; crochet thread

[8-9 A] Framed Greetings set; Filigree background stamp; White vellum, Brocade Blue, Chocolate Chip, Ultrasmooth Vanilla, and Creamy Caramel card stock; Brocade Blue and Chocolate Chip Classic pads; Stampin' Pastels; blender pens; Stampin' Dimensionals; Neutrals Fancy Fibers; Earth Elements eyelets

[8-9 B] Gladsome Garden and Sassy Sayings II sets; Posies & Polka Dots wheel; Really Rust, Creamy Caramel, Chocolate Chip, Old Olive, and Ultrasmooth Vanilla card stock; Chocolate Chip, Really Rust, and Old Olive Craft pads; Creamy Caramel jumbo cartridge; Stampin' Dimensionals; watercolor brush; Neutrals and Earth Elements buttons; linen thread; Natural hemp twine; 1/16" Circle punch; sanding blocks; Stampin' Dimensionals

[8-9 C] Rhyme Time set; By Definition background stamp; Ultrasmooth Vanilla, Chocolate Chip, and Brocade Blue card stock; Earth Elements Trapezoid boxes & tags; Chocolate Chip and Brocade Blue Classic pads; 1/2" Circle punch; Square eyelets; Creamy grosgrain ribbon; linen thread; Stampin' Dimensionals

[8-9 D] Gladsome Garden and Simple Sayings sets; Chocolate Chip, Ultrasmooth Vanilla, and Really Rust card stock; Chocolate Chip, and Brocade Blue Craft pads; VersaMark pad; Silver brads; Classy Copper embossing powder; stamping sponge; linen thread; Earths beads; Stampin' Dimensionals; needle; Earth Elements buttons

[10-11] A Little Engine, Classic Alphabet, and Pure & Simple Alphabet Lower sets; Brilliant Blue, Real Red, Yoyo Yellow, and Ultrasmooth White card stock; Yoyo Yellow, Real Red, and Brilliant Blue Craft pads; Basic Black journaler; Star eyelets; crochet thread; needle

[10-11 B] I'm Here, Classic Alphabet, and Newsprint sets; Hand Prints wheel; Real Red, Brilliant Blue, Yoyo Yellow, and Ultrasmooth White card stock; Basic Black Classic pad; Real Red and Brilliant Blue Craft pads; Brilliant Blue ink cartridge; Basic Black journaler; watercolor brush; 1/4" Circle punch; Bold Brights buttons; Stampin' Dimensionals; Vellum Square Aluminum Metal Edge tags; Royal grosgrain ribbon

[10-11 C] Sporting Goods, Classic Alphabet, and Newsprint sets; Sports Fans wheel; Real Red, Brilliant Blue, Kraft, and Ultrasmooth White card stock; Ultrasmooth tag sheets; Chocolate Chip, Brilliant Blue, and Real Red Craft pads; Basic Black journaler; Night of Navy cartridge; Stampin' Dimensionals; Natural hemp twine; linen thread; Bold Brights I eyelets; crochet thread

[15 A] Birthday Best set; More Mustard, Perfect Plum, Naturals Ivory, and Ruby Red card stock; Basic Black, Mellow Moss, Ruby Red, Perfect Plum, and More Mustard Classic pads; Perfect Plum and More Mustard markers; Square eyelets; Soft Subtles I, Soft Subtles II, and Earth Elements eyelets; Stampin' Dimensionals; watercolor brush; 26-gauge Wire Works; Regals beads; crochet thread

[15 B] Stippled Stencils and Many Thanks sets; Perfect Plum, More Mustard, and Ultrasmooth Vanilla card stock; Soft Subtles mulberry paper; More Mustard, Perfect Plum, and Old Olive Classic pads; watercolor brush; Gold brads; Brass Metal Magic tags

[15 C] Stippled Stencils and Good Times sets; More Mustard, Mellow Moss, and Naturals Ivory card stock; Earth Elements Pouch boxes & tags; More Mustard, Ruby Red, and Mellow Moss Classic pads; linen thread; Stampin' Dimensionals; 1/16" Circle punch; needle

[15 D] Listen with the Heart set; Ruby Red, Perfect Plum, Mellow Moss, and Naturals Ivory card stock; Perfect Plum and Ruby Red Craft pads; Crystal Clear embossing powder; watercolor brush; Square eyelets; Stampin' Dimensionals; Natural hemp twine

[16 A] Festive Four, Itty Bitty Backgrounds, and Everyday Flexible Phrases sets; Brocade Blue, Lavender Lace, and Naturals White card stock; Basic Black, Perfect Plum, Lavender Lace, Brocade Blue, Pretty in Pink, and Sage Shadow Classic pads; watercolor brush; Stampin' Dimensionals; Stainless Steel Metal Magic tags; Silver brads; Soft Subtles II eyelets; Crystal Effects; Silver cord; sanding blocks; sewing machine and thread

[16 B] Wee Watercolors and Good Times sets; Barely Banana, Naturals Ivory, Sage Shadow, and Lavender Lace card stock; Lavender Lace and Sage Shadow Classic pads; Vanilla Craft pad; watercolor brush; Stampin' Dimensionals; 1/16" Circle punch; crochet thread

[16 C] Sculpted Style set; Sage Shadow, Brocade Blue, Lavender Lace, White vellum, and Naturals Ivory card stock; Basic Black, Lavender Lace, Brocade Blue, and Sage Shadow Classic pads; watercolor brush; Stampin' Dimensionals; Light Blue 3/8" organdy ribbon

[16 D] Sculpted Style and Classic Alphabet sets; Barely Banana, Sage Shadow, White vellum, and Brocade Blue card stock; White vellum tag sheets; Basic Black Classic pad; Brocade Blue, Barely Banana, and Sage Shadow Craft pads; watercolor brush; Neutrals Fancy Fibers; Stampin' Dimensionals; Soft Subtles I eyelets

[17 A] Burst into Bloom and Sassy Sayings I sets; Brocade Blue, Sage Shadow, and Naturals Ivory card stock; Sage Shadow, Brocade Blue, and Vanilla Craft pads; VersaMark pad; Stampin' Dimensionals; paper crimper; Concave Square punch

[17 B] Burst into Bloom and Everyday Flexible Phrases sets; Barely Banana, Naturals Ivory, and Lavender Lace card stock; Sage Shadow, Lavender Lace, and Brocade Blue Classic pads; paper crimper; Soft Subtles buttons; Stampin' Dimensionals; Light Orchid grosgrain ribbon; crochet thread

[17 C] Pure & Simple Alphabet Upper sets; In Full Bloom Simply Scrappin' kit; White Vellum card stock; Brocade Blue Craft pad; Basic Black journaler; Ivory 3/8" organdy ribbon; Stampin' Dimensionals; Soft Subtles I eyelets

[18 A] Sweet of You set; Hand-Stitched background stamp; Bliss Blue, White vellum, and Confetti White card stock; Soft Subtles Mini Gable boxes & tags; Basic Black, Bliss Blue, Barely Banana, Summer Sun, Sage Shadow, Brocade Blue, and Ruby Red Classic pads; watercolor brush; Stampin' Dimensionals; Scallop scissors; Cream grosgrain ribbon; 1/16" and 1/8" Circle punches; Soft Subtles II eyelets; crochet thread

[18 B] Sweet of You and Itty Bitty Backgrounds sets; Ruby Red, Sage Shadow, and Confetti White card stock; Basic Black, Ruby Red, Bliss Blue, Creamy Caramel, Sage Shadow, and Barely Banana Classic pads; watercolor brush; 1/16" Circle punch; linen thread; Rich Regals buttons; Stampin' Dimensionals; needle

[18 C] Flower Garden and Classic Alphabet sets; Filigree and Simple Stripes background stamps; Barely Banana, Sage Shadow, Ruby Red, and Confetti White card stock; White mulberry paper; Barely Banana, Ruby Red, Basic Black, Summer Sun, Sage Shadow, and Forest Foliage Classic pads; watercolor brush; Cranberry grosgrain ribbon; 1/16" Circle punch; linen thread

[18 D] Flower Garden and All-Year Cheer I sets; Hand-Stitched background stamp; Confetti White card stock; Soft Subtles Favor boxes & tags; Ballet Blue, Bliss Blue, Sage Shadow, Basic Black, and Summer Sun Classic pads; watercolor brush; Light Blue 3/8" organdy ribbon; Stampin' Dimensionals; thread

[19 A] Suitable for Framing and Contemporary Alphabet sets; Barely Banana, Ruby Red, Sage Shadow, Confetti White, and Bliss Blue card stock; Confetti tag sheets; Barely Banana, Ruby Red, and Bliss Blue Craft pads; Stampin' Dimensionals; Soft Subtles II and Square eyelets; Cream grosgrain ribbon; Write Me a Memory Journaling Fonts CD, Volume I; sewing machine and thread

[19 B] Suitable for Framing and Simple Type Alphabet sets; Sage Shadow, Barely Banana, and Ruby Red card stock; Ruby Red and Sage Shadow Craft pads; Sage Shadow journaler; skeleton leaves; Square eyelets; Natural hemp twine; Stampin' Dimensionals; 1/16" Circle punch

[19 C (5" X 3-3/4")] Suitable for Framing and Everyday Flexible Phrases sets; Barely Banana, Ruby Red, and Ultrasmooth White card stock; Barely Banana, Ruby Red, and Sage Shadow markers; Soft Subtles I eyelets; Stampin' Dimensionals

[19 D] Suitable for Framing, Itty Bitty Backgrounds, and Tiny Talk sets; White vellum and Confetti White card stock; Sage Shadow and Bliss Blue Classic pads; White Craft pad; White 3/8" organdy ribbon; Stampin' Dimensionals; Dazzling Diamonds glitter; crochet thread

[20 A] Botanical Garden and Wonderful Words sets; Mellow Moss, White vellum, and Rose Red card stock; Soft Subtles mulberry paper; VersaMark pad; Rose Red and Old Olive Classic pads; watercolor brush; Winter White embossing powder; Stampin' Dimensionals; Silver cord; 1/16" Circle punch

[20 B] Little Layers Plus and Contemporary Alphabet sets; Pretty in Pink, Rose Red, Ultrasmooth White, Ballet Blue, and Mellow Moss card stock; Pretty in Pink Rose Red, Ballet Blue, and Mellow Moss Craft pads; Basic Black journaler; Stampin' Dimensionals; Small and Large Flower eyelets

[20 C] Little Layers Plus and Vogue Verses sets; Ultrasmooth White and Ballet Blue card stock; Positively Pink, Ballet Blue, and Rose Red Classic pads; Rose grosgrain ribbon; Bold Brights II eyelets; Dazzling Diamonds ribbon

[21 A] Tag Time set; Rose Red, Confetti White, and White vellum card stock; Rich Regals Trapezoid boxes & tags; Ballet Blue Classic pad; Mellow Moss, Ballet Blue, Positively Pink, Rose Red, Barely Banana, and Basic Black markers; Large Flower eyelets; Bluebird grosgrain ribbon; Bold Brights II eyelets; Stampin' Dimensionals

[21 B] Tag Time set; Mellow Moss, Rose Red, Confetti White, and White vellum card stock; Confetti tag sheets; Mellow Moss, Basic Black, Rose Red, Rose Romance, Ballet Blue, and Old Olive Classic pads; watercolor brush; 1/2" Circle punch; Basic eyelets; Rose grosgrain ribbon; Stampin' Dimensionals; 26-gauge Wire Works; sewing machine and thread

[21 C] Tag Time set; Pretty in Pink and Rose Red card stock; Confetti tag sheets; Rose Red Classic pads; Stampin' Dimensionals; Rich Regals eyelets; Red hemp twine

[21 D] Tag Time and All-Year Cheer II sets; Pretty in Pink card stock; Confetti tag sheets; Basic Black, Positively Pink, Pretty in Pink, Blush Blossom, and Yoyo Yellow Classic pads; White Craft pad; watercolor brush; Light Pink grosgrain ribbon; Subtles Fancy Fibers; Stampin' Dimensionals; Soft Subtles I eyelets

[22 A] Ageless Adornment set; More Mustard, Garden Green, and Confetti White card stock; Earth Elements tag sheets; Rich Regals mulberry paper; Bold Brights Pouch boxes & tags; Basic Black, Forest Foliage, Garden Green, More Mustard, Close to Cocoa, Real Red, and Baroque Burgundy Classic pads; watercolor brush; Stampin' Dimensionals; 1/16" Circle punch; linen thread; Earth Elements eyelets; twigs

[22 B] Ageless Adornment and Itty Bitty Backgrounds sets; Filigree background stamp; More Mustard, Not Quite Navy, Real Red, and Confetti White card stock; Basic Black, Sage Shadow, Garden Green, Real Red, More Mustard, and Not Quite Navy Classic pads; watercolor brush; Stampin' Dimensionals; Gold brads; Gold 3/8" organdy ribbon

[22 C] Ageless Adornment set; Real Red, More Mustard, Not Quite Navy, and Confetti White card stock; Night of Navy Classic pad; Earth Elements buttons; linen thread; Stampin' Dimensionals; Red grosgrain ribbon; paper crimper

[23 A] What Could Be Better set; Not Quite Navy, Real Red, Ultrasmooth White, and White vellum card stock; Not Quite Navy Classic pad; Garden Green and Real Red markers; paper crimper; Silver brads; Stampin' Dimensionals; Red grosgrain ribbon

[23 B] What Could Be Better and Pure & Simple Alphabet Lower sets; Real Red, Not Quite Navy, More Mustard, and Ultrasmooth White card stock; Real Red, Not Quite Navy, Garden Green, and More Mustard Craft pads; VersaMark pad; Earth Elements buttons; Red grosgrain ribbon; Write Me a Memory Journaling Fonts CD, Volume I; window sheets; crochet thread; sewing machine and thread

[28 B] Sweet Talk set; Rose Romance, Ultrasmooth White, and Real Red card stock; Rose Romance and Real Red Classic pads; Jet Black StazOn pad; Stampin' Dimensionals; Stainless Steel Metal Magic tags, Assortment II; paper crimper; 22-gauge Wire Works; White grosgrain ribbon

[28 A] Sweet Talk and Pure & Simple Alphabet Lower sets; Real Red, Ultrasmooth White, Rose Red, and Pretty in Pink card stock; Real Red, Eggplant Envy, and Rose Romance Classic pads; VersaMark pad; Brights embossing stack; Stampin' Dimensionals; Red grosgrain ribbon

[28 C] True Love set; French Script background stamp; Eggplant Envy, Confetti White, and Going Gray card stock; Soft Subtles mulberry paper; Confetti tag sheets; Basic Black, Eggplant Envy, Rose Romance, Brocade Blue, and Going Gray Classic pads; watercolor brush; Silver 3/8" organdy ribbon; Stampin' Dimensionals; crochet thread

[29 A] Loving Hearts and Alphadots sets; Rose Romance, Eggplant Envy, and Ultrasmooth White card stock; Rose Red, Eggplant Envy, and Rose Romance Craft pads; Stampin' Dimensionals; Basic eyelets; Write Me a Memory Journaling Fonts CD, Volume I

[29 B] Smitten set; Rose Romance, Pretty in Pink, Ultrasmooth White, and White vellum card stock; Rose Romance and Rose Red Classic pads; Soft Subtles I eyelets; Subtles Fancy Fibers; Stampin' Dimensionals; sewing machine and thread

[29 C] Smitten set; All Heart wheel; Ultrasmooth White card stock; Bold Brights Mini Gable boxes & tags; Real Red Classic pad; Real Red cartridge; Stainless Steel Metal Magic tags; White Square Aluminum Metal Edge tags; Silver brads; Stampin' Dimensionals; 22-gauge Wire Works; 1/8" Circle punch; White grosgrain ribbon

[30 A] Have a Heart set; Lavender Lace, Confetti White, Cameo Coral, and Sage Shadow card stock; Basic Black, Going Gray, Lavender Lace, Bliss Blue, Yoyo Yellow, and Cameo Coral Classic pads; Lavender Lace and Cameo Coral markers; watercolor brush; Stampin' Dimensionals; Large Flower eyelets; Light Orchid grosgrain ribbon

[30 B] Happy Hearts and Good Times sets; Hugs & Kisses wheel; Lavender Lace, Cameo Coral, and Ultrasmooth White card stock; Lavender Lace Classic pad; Cameo Coral cartridge; Lavender Lace marker; White Square Aluminum Metal Edge tags; paper crimper; air art tool; 1/16" and 3/8" Circle punch; Stampin' Dimensionals; crochet thread

[30 C] Happy Hearts and All-Year Cheer I sets; Lavender Lace, Barely Banana, Confetti White, and Cameo Coral card stock; Cameo Coral and Barely Banana Classic pads; White Circle Aluminum Metal Edge tags; Soft Subtles II eyelets; 26-gauge Wire Works; Stampin' Dimensionals; Rose grosgrain ribbon

[31 A] Spring Fling and Pure & Simple Alphabet Upper sets; Barely Banana, Sage Shadow, Lavender Lace, Cameo Coral, and Ultrasmooth White card stock; Lavender Lace, Cameo Coral, and Barely Banana Classic pads; Lavender Lace, Cameo Coral, and Sage Shadow markers; Stampin' Dimensionals; Write Me a Memory Font CD, Volume I; Bold Brights II eyelets; sewing machine and thread

[31 B] Hearts & Clovers set; Sage Shadow, Barely Banana, White vellum, and Confetti White card stock; Confetti tag sheets; Sage Shadow Classic pad; Ivory 7/8" organdy ribbon; Stampin' Dimensionals; sewing machine and thread; crochet thread

[31 C] Hearts & Clovers and Good Times sets; Sage Shadow, Confetti White, and Barely Banana card stock; Basic Black, Orchid Opulence, and Sage Shadow Classic pads; Metal Magic tags; Soft Subtles II eyelets; Stampin' Dimensionals; Light Orchid grosgrain ribbon; crochet thread

[32 A] Renewed Faith set; Filigree background stamp; Lavender Lace, Barely Banana, White vellum, and Confetti White card stock; Basic Black and Lavender Lace Classic pads; VersaMark pad; Crystal Clear embossing powder; Stampin' Dimensionals; White 3/8" organdy ribbon

[32 B] Spring Gifts set; Ballet Blue, Gable Green, Confetti White, and Lavender Lace card stock; Basic Black, Close to Cocoa, Gable Green, Pretty in Pink, Lavender Lace, Ballet Blue, and Going Gray Classic pads; Basic Black marker; watercolor brush; 1/8" Circle punch; Stampin' Dimensionals; Bluebird grosgrain ribbon; Rich Regals buttons; sewing machine and thread; crochet thread

[32 C] Spring Gifts and All-Year Cheer I sets; Spring Things wheel; Barely Banana, Confetti White, and Lavender Lace card stock; Basic Black, Lavender Lace, Pretty in Pink, Barely Banana, Gable Green, Close to Cocoa, and Bliss Blue Classic pads; Lavender Lace cartridge; Stampin' Dimensionals; Bold Brights buttons; White 3/8" organdy ribbon; watercolor brush; crochet thread

[33 A] Halloween Smiles and Background Basics sets; Lavender Lace, Gable Green, Confetti White, and Ballet Blue card stock; Lavender Lace, Basic Black, More Mustard, Only Orange, Going Gray, Garden Green, and Gable Green Classic pads; Basic Black marker; watercolor brush; Light Orchid grosgrain ribbon

[33 B] Carved & Candlelit and Tiny Talk sets; Gable Green, Lavender Lace, Barely Banana, and Confetti White card stock; Only Orange, Basic Black, and Gable Green Classic pad; White Square Aluminum Metal Edge tags; 22-gauge Wire Works; paper crimper; Stampin' Dimensionals

[33 C] Carved & Candlelit and Pure & Simple Alphabet Lower sets; Lavender Lace, Confetti White, Barely Banana, and Gable Green card stock; Only Orange, Gable Green, and Lavender Lace Craft pads; Lavender Lace marker; air art tool; Stampin' Dimensionals; Write Me a Memory Journaling Fonts CD, Volume I; sewing machine and thread

[34 A] Trick or Treat and All-Year Cheer III sets; Eggplant Envy, Old Olive, and Ultrasmooth White card stock; Eggplant Envy Classic pad; Basic Black marker; VersaMark pad; Black embossing powder; Stampin' Dimensionals; Black Magic Mesh

[34 B] Bitty Boos, Classic Alphabet, and Newsprint Alphabet sets; Eggplant Envy, Only Orange, Summer Sun, White vellum, and Basic Black card stock; White and Basic Black Craft pads; Black hemp twine; Write Me a Memory Journaling Fonts CD, Volume I

[35 A] Sweeter Treaters set; Basic Black, Only Orange, Eggplant Envy, and Ultrasmooth White card stock; Basic Black, Summer Sun, Eggplant Envy, Only Orange, Close to Cocoa, Real Red, Old Olive, and Going Gray Classic pads; VersaMark pad; Basic Black marker; Pearl Ex Assortment III; Stainless Steel Metal Magic tags, Assortment I; Neutrals buttons; linen thread; Stampin' Dimensionals; watercolor brush

[35 B] Sweeter Treaters, Halloween Backgrounds, and All-Year Cheer II sets; Old Olive, Ultrasmooth White, and Only Orange card stock; Basic Black, Only Orange, Old Olive, Creamy Caramel, Summer Sun, and Blush Blossom Classic pads; Stampin' Dimensionals; watercolor brush; White grosgrain ribbon

[35 C] Halloween Backgrounds and All-Year Cheer III sets; Ultrasmooth White card stock; Earth Elements Mini Gable boxes & tags; Basic Black and Only Orange Classic pads; window sheets; Bold Brights II eyelets; Tangerine grosgrain ribbon

[36 A] Mazel Tov set; Ruby Red, More Mustard, and Naturals Ivory card stock; Ruby Red Classic pad; VersaMark pad; Earth Tones embossing stack; watercolor brush; 1/16" Circle punch; Earth Elements button; 26-gauge Wire Works

[36 B] Festive Hanukkah set; Brocade Blue, Naturals Ivory, and More Mustard card stock; VersaMark pad; Ballet Blue Classic pad; Earth Tones embossing stack; White 3/8" organdy ribbon; Stampin' Dimensionals

[36 C] Festive Hanukkah set; Naturals Ivory card stock; Earth Elements Favor boxes & tags; VersaMark pad; More Mustard marker; Gold detail embossing powder; 1/16" Circle punch; Gold cord

[37 A] Little Holiday Wishes set; Brocade Blue, Ruby Red, Garden Green, More Mustard, and Naturals Ivory card stock; Basic Black, More Mustard, Brocade Blue, Garden Green, and Ruby Red Classic pads; Ballet Blue marker; watercolor brush; paper crimper; 1/4" Circle punch; Cream grosgrain ribbon; Stampin' Dimensionals; Crystal Effects

[37 B] Sweet Holidays set; Holiday Sweets wheel; Ruby Red, More Mustard, Garden Green, and Naturals Ivory card stock; Basic Black, Garden Green, Creamy Caramel, Ruby Red, More Mustard, and Bordering Blue Classic pads; Ruby Red cartridge; Star eyelets; Red grosgrain ribbon; Stampin' Dimensionals; Dazzling Diamonds glitter

[37 C] Sweet Holidays and Contemporary Alphabet sets; Garden Green, Ruby Red, and Naturals Ivory card stock; Ruby Red, Garden Green, and Creamy Caramel Craft pads; Ruby Red marker; watercolor brush; Red grosgrain ribbon; Bold Brights eyelets; crochet thread

[38 A] Frosty set; Sage Shadow, Brocade Blue, and Confetti White card stock; White Craft pad; Basic Black, Going Gray, Sage Shadow, Brocade Blue, Bordering Blue, Real Red, and Only Orange Classic pads; watercolor brush; White Circle Aluminum Metal Edge tags; Stampin' Dimensionals; 26-gauge Wire Works; crochet thread

[38 B] Crazy for Christmas set; Groovy Lines background stamp; Real Red, Confetti White, Brocade Blue, and Sage Shadow card stock; Basic Black, Brocade Blue, Real Red, and Sage Shadow Classic pads; watercolor brush; Real Red marker; 1/16" Circle punch; Stampin' Dimensionals; Brights Fancy Fibers; crochet thread

[38 C] Crazy for Christmas set; Brocade Blue, Sage Shadow, Real Red, White vellum, and Ultrasmooth White card stock; Basic Black, Sage Shadow, Not Quite Navy, and Baroque Burgundy Classic pads; Silver brads

[39 A] Yule Bits & Borders set; Brocade Blue, Brushed silver, and Confetti White card stock; Brocade Blue Classic pad; Silver metallic pad; Silver cord; Basic eyelets; 22-gauge Wire Works; Stampin' Dimensionals

[39 B] Yule Bits & Borders and Pure & Simple Alphabet Lower sets; Real Red, Sage Shadow, and Confetti White card stock; Real Red and Sage Shadow Craft pads; VersaMark pad; Write Me a Memory Journaling Fonts CD, Volume I; Brights Fancy Fibers; Stampin' Dimensionals; White Square Brass Metal Edge tags

[39 C] Very Merry set; Heart Angels wheel; Confetti White, Real Red, and Sage Shadow card stock; Bold Brights tag sheets; Basic Black, Real Red, Sage Shadow, Yoyo Yellow, and Blush Blossom Classic pads; Sage Shadow cartridge; watercolor brush; Dazzling Diamonds glitter; Stampin' Dimensionals; Folk Heart punch; 1/16" Circle punch; White grosgrain ribbon

[40 A] Season's Sketches and All-Year Cheer I sets; Not Quite Navy, Old Olive, Baroque Burgundy, and Confetti White card stock; Old Olive and Not Quite Navy Classic pads; paper crimper; Natural hemp twine; 1/16" Circle punch; Stampin' Dimensionals

[40 B] Holiday Woodcuts set; Christmas Time wheel; Confetti White and More Mustard card stock; Earth Elements Pouch boxes & tags; More Mustard and Baroque Burgundy Classic pads; Old Olive cartridge; Earth Elements eyelets; 1/8" Circle punch; Cranberry grosgrain ribbon; Stampin' Dimensionals; sewing machine and thread

[41 A] Holiday Sampler set; Not Quite Navy, More Mustard, Eggplant Envy, and Confetti White card stock; Not Quite Navy and Old Olive Classic pads; VersaMark pad; Regal Tones embossing stack; paper crimper; 1/16" Circle punch; Stampin' Dimensionals; 1-1/4" Circle punch; Vellum Circle Aluminum Metal Edge tags; 22-gauge Wire Works; Silver cord

[41 B] Sparkling Season set; Candy Cane Craze wheel; Baroque Burgundy, Old Olive, and Confetti White card stock; Basic Black, More Mustard, Baroque Burgundy, and Old Olive markers; Baroque Burgundy cartridge; White Square Aluminum Metal Edge tags; Stampin' Dimensionals; Earths Fancy Fibers; Write Me a Memory Journaling Fonts CD, Volume I

[42 A] Ho-Ho-Holidays set; Ruby Red, Confetti Cream, Mellow Moss, and Eggplant Envy card stock; Basic Black, Eggplant Envy, Yoyo Yellow, Mellow Moss, Ruby Red, Blush Blossom, Going Gray, Creamy Caramel, and Close to Cocoa Classic pads; watercolor brush; Stampin' Dimensionals; Earth Elements buttons; needle; crochet thread

[42 B] Flaky Friends set; Many Mittens wheel; Kraft medium gift box; Ruby Red, Creamy Caramel, Eggplant Envy, and Confetti Cream card stock; Earth Elements tag sheets; Basic Black, Eggplant Envy, More Mustard, Going Gray, Ruby Red, Creamy Caramel, Mellow Moss, and Only Orange Classic pads; Creamy Caramel cartridge; Basic Black marker; watercolor brush; 1/16" and 1/8" Circle punches; natural hemp twine; Stampin' Dimensionals; Soft Subtles I eyelets; crochet thread; needle

[42 C] Flaky Friends set; Eggplant Envy, Creamy Caramel, and Confetti Cream card stock; Earth Elements tag sheets; Basic Black, Eggplant Envy, Ruby Red, Mellow Moss, Bordering Blue, More Mustard, Only Orange, and Creamy Caramel Classic pads; watercolor brush; Natural hemp twine; Soft Subtles I eyelets; window sheet; sewing machine and thread

[43 A] Star of Wonder set; Creamy Caramel, Eggplant Envy, White vellum, and Confetti Cream card stock; Eggplant Envy and Creamy Caramel Classic pads; 1/16" Circle punch; Stampin' Dimensionals; White Square Brass Metal Edge tags; 26-gauge Wire Works; Southwest corner punch

[43 B] Holiday Print stamp; Ruby Red, Mellow Moss, Eggplant Envy, Confetti Cream, and Brushed silver card stock; Ruby Red Classic pad; paper crimper; Stampin' Dimensionals; 26-gauge Wire Works; Regals beads

[44 A] Happy Winter and Tiny Talk sets; Baroque Burgundy, Confetti Cream, Sage Shadow, and Creamy Caramel card stock; Basic Black, Sage Shadow, Creamy Caramel, and Baroque Burgundy Classic pads; watercolor brush; 1/16" Circle punch; Natural hemp twine; Stampin' Dimensionals

[44 B] Angelic set; French Script background stamp; Creamy Caramel, Confetti Cream, and Baroque Burgundy card stock; Creamy Caramel and Baroque Burgundy Classic pads; Rich Regals and Earth Elements mulberry paper; Stampin' Dimensionals; Gold brads

[45 A] Sleigh Ride set; Creamy Caramel, Sage Shadow, Confetti Cream, and Baroque Burgundy card stock; Basic Black, Creamy Caramel, More Mustard, Ruby Red, Sage Shadow, Bordering Blue, and Close to Cocoa Classic pads; watercolor brush; Stampin' Dimensionals; Gold brads

[45 B] Holiday Wishes and All-Year Cheer I sets; Baroque Burgundy, More Mustard, and Sage Shadow card stock; Baroque Burgundy Classic pad; VersaMark pad; Crystal Clear embossing powder; Natural hemp twine; Stampin' Dimensionals; Rich Regals buttons; 1/16" Circle punch

[46 A] Christmas Foliage set; Night of Navy, Confetti White, and Baroque Burgundy card stock; Night of Navy and Baroque Burgundy Classic pads; Cranberry grosgrain ribbon; Large Circle eyelets

[46 B] Holiday Basics and Pure & Simple Alphabet Lower sets; Funky Firs wheel; Sage Shadow, Baroque Burgundy, and More Mustard card stock; More Mustard, Garden Green, and Baroque Burgundy Craft pads; Garden Green cartridge; Stampin' Dimensionals; Natural hemp twine; Write Me a Memory Journaling Fonts CD, Volume I

[47 A] Magic & Wonder and Good Times sets; Hand-Stitched background stamp; Confetti White and Baroque Burgundy card stock; Confetti White tag sheet; Basic Black, Baroque Burgundy, Blush Blossom, More Mustard, Garden Green, Close to Cocoa, Creamy Caramel, and Brocade Blue Classic pads; watercolor brush; 1/8" Circle punch; Wine 3/8" organdy ribbon

[47 B] Holiday Spirit set; Only Ornaments wheel; Night of Navy, Garden Green, Baroque Burgundy, and Confetti White card stock; Night of Navy and Garden Green Classic pads; Night of Navy cartridge; paper crimper; 1/16" Circle punch; Natural hemp twine; Stampin' Dimensionals

[47 C] Holiday Spirit set; Confetti White and Sage Shadow card stock; Rich Regals Mini Gable boxes & tags; Basic Black, Sage Shadow, Night of Navy, and Baroque Burgundy Classic pads; watercolor brush; Stampin' Dimensionals; Silver cord

[48 A] Christmas Gift Tags set; Confetti White card stock; Soft Subtles and White vellum tag sheets; Basic Black, Mellow Moss, Rose Red, Brocade Blue, Creamy Caramel, and Almost Amethyst Classic pad; Rose Red marker; watercolor brush; White Square Aluminum Metal Edge tags; Large Circle eyelets; Subtles Fancy Fibers; Silver cord; sewing machine and thread

[48 B] Christmas Gift Tags set; Rose Red card stock; Soft Subtles tag sheets; Mellow Moss Classic pad; Ruby Red marker; Soft Subtles I eyelets; Spring Moss grosgrain ribbon

[48 C] Christmas Gift Tags set; Candy Cane Christmas wheel; Mellow Moss and Ultrasmooth White card stock; Glossy White basket box; Rose Red and Mellow Moss Classic pads; Rose Red cartridge; paper crimper; Large Circle eyelets; White 3/8" organdy ribbon; Stampin' Dimensionals

[49 A] Snowy Play set; Brocade Blue, Confetti White, Rose Red, and Almost Amethyst card stock; Basic Black, Rose Red, Creamy Caramel, Close to Cocoa, Only Orange, Bordering Blue, Going Gray, and Brocade Blue Classic pads; Basic Black marker; watercolor brush; Square eyelets

[49 B] Lace Snowflakes, Journaling Fun, and Newsprint Alphabet sets; Brocade Blue, Almost Amethyst, Confetti White, and Mellow Moss card stock; Almost Amethyst, Brocade Blue, and White Craft pads; VersaMark pad; Almost Amethyst marker; White Circle Aluminum Metal Edge tags; Basic eyelets; Neutrals Fancy Fibers; stamping sponge; Stampin' Dimensionals

[50 A] A Beautiful Season set; Bordering Blue, Ultrasmooth White, and White vellum card stock; Bordering Blue Classic pad; 1-3/8" Circle punch; 1/8" Circle punch; Rich Regals eyelets; White 3/8" organdy ribbon; Dazzling Diamonds glitter; spray mount

[50 B] A Beautiful Season set; Chocolate Chip, Creamy Caramel, Mellow Moss, and Confetti White card stock; Chocolate Chip Craft pad; Close to Cocoa, Mellow Moss, and Old Olive Classic pads; air art tool, Square eyelets; Natural hemp twine; Stampin' Dimensionals; 1/8" Circle punch; sanding block

[50 C] A Beautiful Season set; Pine Bough wheel; Creamy Caramel, Mellow Moss, Chocolate Chip, and Confetti White card stock; Chocolate Chip cartridge; Close to Cocoa, Creamy Caramel, Mellow Moss, Old Olive, and Basic Brown Classic pads; watercolor brush; 1/2" Circle punch; Large Circle eyelets; Soft Subtles I eyelets; Natural hemp twine

[51 A] Snowflakes set; Bordering Blue card stock; Bordering Blue Craft pads; Rich Regals eyelets; Basic eyelets; 22-gauge Wire Works; White Circle Aluminum Metal Edge tags; White grosgrain ribbon; Dazzling Diamonds glitter; spray mount

[51 B] Solemn Stillness set; Mellow Moss and Confetti White card stock; Mellow Moss Craft pad; Top Boss pad; Gold detail embossing powder; 1/16" Circle punch; Gold cord

[51 C] Solemn Stillness set; Star Studded wheel; Bordering Blue, Confetti White, and Brushed Gold card stock; White Craft pad; Clear embossing cartridge; Top Boss pad; Gold detail embossing powder; 1/16" Circle punch; Gold cord; Stampin' Dimensionals

[52 A] Spring Party set; Joy of Spring wheel; Eggplant Envy, Not Quite Navy, More Mustard, and Naturals Ivory card stock; Basic Black, Old Olive, Not Quite Navy, Eggplant Envy, Going Gray, and More Mustard Classic pads; StazOn pad; Not Quite Navy cartridge; watercolor brush; Stampin' Dimensionals; Copper Metal Magic tags, Assortment II; linen thread; Spring Moss grosgrain ribbon

[52 B] Simply Spring and Sassy Sayings II sets; Creamy Caramel, Eggplant Envy, Naturals Ivory, and Mellow Moss card stock; Basic Black, Eggplant Envy, and Old Olive Classic pads; watercolor brush; Spring Moss grosgrain ribbon; liquid bleach

[53 A] Summer by the Sea set; Creamy Caramel, Eggplant Envy, Not Quite Navy, and Naturals Ivory card stock; Basic Black and Creamy Caramel Classic pads; watercolor brush; Stampin' Pastels; Stampin' Dimensionals; 1/16" Circle punch; Natural hemp twine

[53 B] Summer by the Sea set; Creamy Caramel, Not Quite Navy, Eggplant Envy, More Mustard, and Naturals Ivory card stock; Basic Black Classic pad; VersaMark pad; Not Quite Navy, Eggplant Envy, Creamy Caramel, More Mustard, and Blush Blossom Craft pads; watercolor brush; Stampin' Dimensionals; Natural hemp twine; Natural Magic Mesh; Write Me a Memory Journaling Fonts CD, Volume I; liquid bleach

[54 A] Seaside Sketches set; Tempting Turquoise, Gable Green, Cameo Coral, and Confetti White card stock; Basic Black, Cameo Coral, Barely Banana, Bliss Blue, Tempting Turquoise, Creamy Caramel, Blush Blossom, Chocolate Chip, and Ballet Blue Classic pads; Tempting Turquoise marker; watercolor brush; natural hemp twine; Stampin' Dimensionals; Regals beads

[54 B] On the Beach and All-Year Cheer II sets; Barely Banana, Gable Green, Cameo Coral, and Confetti White card stock; Basic Black, Gable Green, Cameo Coral, and Barely Banana Classic pads; VersaMark pad; watercolor brush; paper crimper; Stampin' Dimensionals; Cream grosgrain ribbon; 22-gauge Wire Works; 1/16" Circle punch

[55 A] Sparkling Summer and Simple Type Alphabet sets; Cameo Coral, Barely Banana, Tempting Turquoise, and Confetti White card stock; Tempting Turquoise, Basic Black, Barely Banana, Gable Green, Green Galore, Going Gray, and Cameo Coral Craft pads; window sheet; Write Me a Memory Journaling Fonts CD, Volume I; paper crimper; Stampin' Dimensionals; 22-gauge Wire Works; Crystal Effects; Soft Subtles I eyelets; watercolor brush

[55 B] Sparkling Summer and Sassy Sayings II sets; Cameo Coral, Gable Green, Confetti White, Barely Banana, and Tempting Turquoise card stock; Basic Black, Tempting Turquoise, Gable Green, More Mustard, Cameo Coral, and Barely Banana Classic pads; watercolor brush; Stampin' Dimensionals; Dazzling Diamonds glitter; Soft Subtles I eyelets; sewing machine and thread

[55 C] Sparkling Summer and All-Year Cheer II sets; Gable Green, Tempting Turquoise, Confetti White, and Cameo Coral card stock; Soft Subtles Trapezoid boxes & tags; Basic Black, Cameo Coral, Gable Green, Tempting Turquoise, and Barely Banana Classic pads; Cameo Coral and Basic Black markers; watercolor brush; air art tool; 1/16" and 1/8" Circle punches; 22-gauge Wire Works; Stampin' Dimensionals; Crystal Effects; Turquoise grosgrain ribbon; Love without End Classy Brass template

[56 A] Vegetable Garden and Sassy Sayings I sets; Confetti White, Ruby Red, White vellum, and Old Olive card stock; Ruby Red, More Mustard, and Old Olive Craft pads

[56 B] Vegetable Garden set; Summer Sun, Old Olive, Confetti White, and Ruby Red card stock; Old Olive and Ruby Red Craft pads; Basic Black journaler; sewing machine and thread

[56 C] Vegetable Garden and Newsprint sets; Old Olive, Summer Sun, Really Rust, Confetti White, and More Mustard card stock; Earth Elements tag sheets; Old Olive, Really Rust, and Summer Sun Craft pads; Basic Black journaler; Stampin' Dimensionals; linen thread; Earth Elements Buttons

[57 A] Happy Fall, Y'all set; Really Rust, Old Olive, Ruby Red, and Confetti White card stock; Basic Black, Really Rust, More Mustard, Old Olive, Creamy Caramel, and Ruby Red Classic pads; Stampin' Dimensionals; watercolor brush; linen thread; Earths Magic Mesh

[57 B] Fall Whimsy set; Acorns wheel; Ruby Red, Old Olive, Really Rust, and More Mustard card stock; embossing cartridge; Basic Black, Really Rust, Old Olive, and More Mustard Classic pads; watercolor brush; Copper cord; Copper Metal Magic tags; Vellum Circle Copper Metal Edge tags; Classy Copper embossing powder; needle

[57 C] Fall Whimsy and Everyday Flexible Phrases sets; Old Olive, Really Rust, and Confetti White card stock; Soft Subtles mulberry paper; Confetti tag sheets; Really Rust and Old Olive Classic pads; VersaMark pad; Stampin' Pastels; watercolor brush; Stampin' Dimensionals; Earth Elements eyelets; Natural hemp twine; 1/16" Circle punch

[58 A] Vine & Berry and All-Year Cheer III sets; Creamy Caramel, Mellow Moss, and Naturals Ivory card stock; Earth Elements vellum; Creamy Caramel and Mellow Moss Craft pad; Stampin' Dimensionals; Taupe grosgrain ribbon; Copper cord; 22-gauge Wire Works; White Square Copper Metal Edge tags

[58 B] Fancy Foliage, Wonderful Words, and Classic Alphabet sets; More Mustard and Mellow Moss card stock; Soft Subtles vellum; Earth Elements tag sheets; More Mustard and Mellow Moss Craft pads; Crystal Clear embossing powder; Write Me a Memory Journaling Fonts CD, Volume I; skeleton leaves; Olive 3/8" organdy ribbon; Stampin' Dimensionals; 1/8" Circle punch

[59 A] Fall Fun set; More Mustard, Mellow Moss, Creamy Caramel, and Naturals Ivory card stock; VersaMark pad; More Mustard Classic pad; Earth Tones embossing stack; 1/16" Circle punch; Natural hemp twine; Natural Magic Mesh

[59 B] Lovely Leaves and Pure & Simple Alphabet Lower sets; Creamy Caramel, Naturals Ivory, and Mellow Moss card stock; Creamy Caramel Craft pad; VersaMark pad; Crystal Clear embossing powder; White Square Copper Metal Edge tags; paper crimper; Write Me a Memory Journaling Fonts CD, Volume I; Natural hemp twine; Stampin' Dimensionals

[60 A] Wonderful Words sets; Confetti Cream, Mellow Moss, and Close to Cocoa card stock; Basic Black, Going Gray, Bordering Blue, Ruby Red, More Mustard, Close to Cocoa, Creamy Caramel, and Mellow Moss Classic pads; watercolor brush; 1/8" Circle punch; natural hemp twine

[60 B] Little Somethings and Simple Sayings II sets; Pindot wheel; Bordering Blue, Ruby Red, and Confetti Cream card stock; Rich Regals and Earth Elements eyelets; Basic Black, Bordering Blue, Ruby Red, Close to Cocoa, and Night of Navy Classic pads; Basic Black cartridge; watercolor brush; Soft Subtles eyelets; Stampin' Dimensionals; Natural hemp twine

[61 A] A Tree for All Seasons and Tiny Talk sets; Stipple Plaid background stamp; Confetti Cream card stock; Soft Subtles Mini Gable boxes & tags; Soft Subtles tag sheets; window sheets; Basic Black, Mellow Moss, Ruby Red, Close to Cocoa, Bordering Blue, and Creamy Caramel Classic pads; watercolor brush; White Square Aluminum Metal Edge tags; paper crimper; 1/16" Circle punch; Natural hemp twine; Stampin' Dimensionals

[61 B] Sweet Seasons and All-Year Cheer III sets; Filigree background stamp; Bordering Blue, White vellum, Confetti Cream, and Ruby Red card stock; Soft Subtles tag sheets; Basic Black, Brocade Blue, Ruby Red, Bordering Blue, Blush Blossom, Close to Cocoa, Creamy Caramel, Only Orange, and Mellow Moss Classic pads; watercolor brush; Notched corner punch; Celery 3/8" organdy ribbon; Stampin' Dimensionals

[61 C] Sweet Seasons and All-Year Cheer I sets; Hand-Stitched background stamp; Ruby Red, Close to Cocoa, Confetti Cream, and Mellow Moss card stock; Basic Black, Ruby Red, Bordering Blue, Creamy Caramel, Mellow Moss, Blush Blossom, and More Mustard Classic pads; watercolor brush; Ivory 7/8" organdy ribbon; Earth Elements buttons

[62 A] A Year in the Country set; Rose Red, Ballet Blue, Sage Shadow, and Confetti White card stock; Garden Green, Basic Black, Ballet Blue, Sage Shadow, Going Gray, Rose Red, Bliss Blue, Mauve Mist, and More Mustard Classic pads; watercolor brush; White Square Aluminum Metal Edge tags; Silver brads

[62 B] Little Layers and Sassy Sayings I sets; Ballet Blue, Rose Red, and Ultrasmooth White card stock; Rose Red, Ballet Blue, and Basic Black Classic pads; paper crimper; Stampin' Dimensionals

[63 A] Shapes & Shadows and All-Year Cheer I sets; Sage Shadow, Rose Red, and Ultrasmooth White card stock; Sage Shadow and Forest Foliage Classic pads; 1/16" Circle punch; Natural hemp twine; Stampin' Dimensionals

[63 B] Shapes & Shadows and Pure & Simple Alphabet Upper sets; Sage Shadow, Ultrasmooth White, Ballet Blue, Rose Red, and Bliss Blue card stock; Ballet Blue, Bliss Blue, Rose Red, and Sage Shadow Craft pads; Basic Black journaler; White Circle Aluminum Metal Edge tags; Large Circle eyelets; Stampin' Dimensionals

[64 A] Window on the World set; Denim background stamp; Confetti White, Taken with Teal, and Old Olive card stock; Basic Black Classic pad; Close to Cocoa, Creamy Caramel, Ruby Red, Taken with Teal, More Mustard, Summer Sun, Old Olive, and Going Gray Craft pads; watercolor brush; Natural hemp twine; linen thread; Earth Elements buttons; needle

[64 B] Little Layers II and Classic Alphabet sets; Confetti White, Ruby Red, and More Mustard Classic pads; Ruby Red, More Mustard, and Basic Black Craft pads; Gold brads; Basic eyelets; 22-gauge Wire Works; Stampin' Dimensionals

[65 A] Sketch It set; Ultrasmooth White, Ruby Red, Old Olive, and White vellum card stock; Old Olive and Ruby Red Classic pads; Top Boss pad; Gold detail embossing powder; Notched Corner punch; Gold cord; Stampin' Dimensionals

[65 B] Sketch It set; Earth Elements Mini Gable boxes & tags; Ultrasmooth White, Old Olive, and Ruby Red card stock; More Mustard, Ruby Red, and Old Olive Classic pads; Earth Elements tag sheets; Natural hemp twine; linen thread; Square eyelets; Stampin' Dimensionals

[65 C] Sketch It set; Earth Elements Trapezoid boxes & tags; Confetti White and Taken with Teal card stock; More Mustard and Taken with Teal Classic pads; Triangle eyelets; Natural hemp twine; watercolor brush; Stampin' Dimensionals; 1/16" Circle punch

[66 A] et; Stipple Plaid background stamp; Gable Green, Eggplant Envy, Positively Pink, and Confetti White card stock; Basic Black, Gable Green, Positively Pink, and Eggplant Envy Classic pads; Stampin' Dimensionals; paper crimper; watercolor brush; Bold Brights buttons; Rose grosgrain ribbon; crochet thread

[66 B] Year-Round Fun II and Tiny Talk sets; Positively Pink and Orchid Opulence card stock; Soft Subtles Pouch boxes & tags; Basic Black Classic pad; Orchid Opulence and Positively Pink Craft pads; Jet Black StazOn pad; watercolor brush; Scallop scissors; Stampin' Dimensionals; Bold Brights II eyelets; 1/8" Circle punch; Light Orchid grosgrain ribbon; Stainless Steel Metal Magic tags, Assortment II; crochet thread

[66 C] Simple Seasons and Sassy Sayings II sets; Confetti White, Positively Pink, and Gable Green card stock; Slumber Party Designer Series paper; Positively Pink and Gable Green Classic pads; Stampin' Dimensionals; Large Flower eyelets

[67 A] Stipple Celebrations and Sassy Saying II sets; Positively Pink, Gable Green, Ultrasmooth White, and Orchid Opulence card stock; Positively Pink, Gable Green, and Orchid Opulence Classic pads; Bold Brights II eyelets; paper crimper; Light Orchid grosgrain ribbon; Brights Magic Mesh

[67 B] Stipple Celebrations and Quirky Alphabet Upper sets; Busy Blocks wheel; Eggplant Envy, Orchid Opulence, Positively Pink, White vellum, Gable Green, and Ultrasmooth White card stock; Positively Pink, Orchid Opulence, Eggplant Envy, and Gable Green Craft pads; Eggplant Envy ink refill; empty jumbo cartridge; Stampin' Dimensionals; Light Orchid and Rose grosgrain ribbon; Write Me a Memory Journaling Fonts CD, Volume I; White Square Aluminum Metal Edge tags

[68 A] Nice & Easy Notes; Rose Romance, Tempting Turquoise, Lavender Lace, and Confetti White card stock; Basic Black, Rose Romance, Tempting Turquoise, Green Galore, Barely Banana, and Lavender Lace Classic pads; Rose Romance marker; watercolor brush; Stampin' Dimensionals; Small Flower eyelets; needle

[68 B] Simple Wishes set; Lavender Lace and Confetti White card stock; White Circle Aluminum Metal Edge tags; Basic Black, Lavender Lace, Rose Romance, Gable Green, and Bliss Blue Classic pads; Lavender Lace marker; watercolor brush; 1/16" Circle punch; Crystal Effects; 22-gauge Wire Works; Stampin' Dimensionals; Apple Green grosgrain ribbon

[69 A] Greetings Galore set; Simple Stripes background stamp; Green Galore, Rose Romance, and Confetti White card stock; Garden Green Classic pad; Green Galore, Rose Romance, Lavender Lace, and Tempting Turquoise markers; Bold Brights II eyelets; Stampin' Dimensionals; 1-3/8" Square punch; Vellum Square Aluminum Metal Edge tags

[69 B] Bitty Bolds and Sassy Sayings I sets; Polka Dot Blocks wheel; Lavender Lace, Tempting Turquoise, Rose Romance, and Ultrasmooth White card stock; Tempting Turquoise and Lavender Lace Classic pads; Rose Romance cartridge; Stampin' Dimensionals; paper crimper; Basic and Bold Brights II eyelets

[70 A] Favorite Teddy Bear and All-Year Cheer I sets; Night of Navy, Creamy Caramel, Garden Green, White vellum, and Confetti White card stock; Basic Black, Chocolate Chip, Night of Navy, and Garden Green Classic pads; watercolor brush; Stampin' Dimensionals; Natural hemp twine; Rich Regals eyelets

[70 B] Favorite Teddy Bear set; Real Red, Confetti White, and Creamy Caramel card stock; Basic Black, Chocolate Chip, Night of Navy, Real Red, Going Gray, and Sage Shadow Classic pads; watercolor brush; Stampin' Dimensionals; 26-gauge Wire Works; Red grosgrain ribbon; 1/8" Circle punch; Natural Magic Mesh

[70 C] Favorite Teddy Bear set; Confetti White, Real Red, and Night of Navy card stock; Earth Elements Pouch boxes & tags; Basic Black, Creamy Caramel, Real Red, Night of Navy, and Garden Green Classic pads; watercolor brush; White Square Aluminum Metal Edge tags; Stampin' Dimensionals; paper crimper; Natural twine; Neutrals buttons

[71 A] Nice & Narrow set; Night of Navy, Garden Green, and Confetti White card stock; Basic Black, Night of Navy, and Garden Green Classic pads; Jet Black StazOn pad; watercolor brush; window sheets; 22-gauge Wire Works; Stampin' Dimensionals; Stainless Steel Metal Magic tags, Assortment II

[71 B] Nice & Narrow set; Garden Green and Confetti White card stock; Bold Brights Trapezoid boxes & tags; Basic Black, Real Red, More Mustard, and Garden Green Classic pads; Stampin' Dimensionals; watercolor brush; 1/8" Circle punch; Red grosgrain ribbon; Bold Brights I eyelets; Brights Fancy Fibers

[71 C] The Fine Print set; By Definition background stamp; Night of Navy, Creamy Caramel, Real Red, and Confetti White card stock; Basic Black, Night of Navy, and Real Red Classic pads; watercolor brush; Bold Brights I eyelets; Stampin' Dimensionals; Natural hemp twine

[72 A] Mini Messages and Simple Type Alphabet sets; Sage Shadow, Garden Green, Brocade Blue, and Ultrasmooth White card stock; Bold Brights pennant sheets; Lovely Lilac and Sage Shadow Craft pads; Purple hemp twine; Stampin' Dimensionals; window sheets; Soft Subtles II eyelets; Write Me a Memory Journaling Fonts CD, Volume I; White Square Aluminum Metal Edge tags

[72 B] Bold Basics and Sassy Sayings I sets; Lovely Lilac, Ultrasmooth White, Garden Green, and Sage Shadow card stock; Lovely Lilac, Sage Shadow, and Garden Green Classic pads; Stampin' Dimensionals

[73 A] Figures of Speech set; Sage Shadow, Brocade Blue, Lovely Lilac, Garden Green, and Confetti White card stock; Basic Black, Brocade Blue, Lovely Lilac, and Sage Shadow Classic pads; watercolor brush; Stampin' Dimensionals; 1/16" Circle punch; Natural hemp twine; Square Aluminum Metal Edge tags

[73 B] Figures of Speech set; Brocade Blue, Mellow Moss, and Confetti White card stock; Bold Brights Pouch boxes & tags; Vellum Circle silver Metal Edge tags; 1-1/4" and 1/16" Circle punches; Lovely Lilac and Brocade Blue Classic pads; watercolor brush; Stampin' Dimensionals; 22-gauge Wire Works

[73 C] Figures of Speech set; Sage Shadow, Confetti White, and Garden Green card stock; Basic Black, Sage Shadow, Garden Green, Creamy Caramel, and Summer Sun Classic pads; watercolor brush; Stampin' Dimensionals; Soft Subtles II eyelets; Earths Fancy Fibers

[73 D] Quick & Cute set; Brocade Blue, Garden Green, Sage Shadow, and Confetti White card stock; Basic Black, Brocade Blue, Sage Shadow, Garden Green, and Barely Banana Classic pads; Jet Black StazOn pad; watercolor brush; paper crimper; Natural hemp twine; Stampin' Dimensionals

[74 A] Vertical Greetings set; Star Studded wheel; Tempting Turquoise, Ultrasmooth White, Positively Pink, Gable Green, and Lovely Lilac card stock; Basic Black Classic pad; Tempting Turquoise ink cartridge; Stampin' Dimensionals; Triangle eyelets; Bold Brights II eyelets; Brights Fancy Fibers

[74 B] On the Line and Beyond the Basics sets; Gable Green, Positively Pink, and Confetti White card stock; Gable Green and Positively Pink Classic pads; White Circle Aluminum Metal Edge tags; Stampin' Dimensionals; Rose grosgrain ribbon; 1/16" Circle punch; 26-gauge Wire Works; Write Me a Memory Journaling Fonts CD, Volume I

[74 C] On the Line and Newsprint sets; Ballet Blue, Tempting Turquoise, and Confetti White card stock; Cameo Coral, Ballet Blue, Tempting Turquoise, and Basic Black Craft pads; Night of Navy marker; White Circle and Square Aluminum Metal Edge tags; Stampin' Dimensionals

[75 A] Simple Somethings, Everyday Flexible Phrases, and Sassy Sayings II sets; Ballet Blue and Gable Green card stock; Confetti tag sheets; Basic Black, Ballet Blue, Taken with Teal, Cameo Coral, Gable Green, and Pretty in Pink Classic pads; watercolor brush; Stampin' Dimensionals; Bold Brights II eyelets; Celery 3/8" organdy ribbon; crochet thread

[75 B] Just My Type, Simple Type Alphabet, and Simple Type Alphabet Numbers; Tempting Turquoise, Confetti White, and Positively Pink card stock; Confetti tag sheets; White, Positively Pink, and Tempting Turquoise Craft pads; Write Me a Memory Journaling Fonts CD, Volume I; Turquoise and Rose grosgrain ribbon; Silver brads; sewing machine and thread

[76 A] Mini Mates set; Natural White, Mauve Mist, and Mellow Moss card stock; VersaMark pad; Mellow Moss and Mauve Mist Classic pads; Hologram Highlights embossing powder; 22- and 26-gauge Wire Works; 1-1/4" Circle punch; Stampin' Dimensionals; stamping sponges; Stainless Steel Metal Magic tags, Assortment II; watercolor brush; needle

[76 B] Mini Mates set; Mauve Mist, Ultrasmooth White, Barely Banana, Mellow Moss, and Bordering Blue card stock; Soft Subtles tag sheets; White craft pad; Mauve Mist, Bordering Blue, Barely Banana, and Mellow Moss Classic pads; window sheets; paper crimper; Subtles Fancy Fibers; Stampin' Dimensionals; 1/2" Circle punch; Soft Subtles I eyelets; crochet thread

[76 C] Tags & More set; Square Pegs wheel; Mellow Moss, Mauve Mist, Bordering Blue, and Confetti White card stock; Basic Black, Mellow Moss, Pretty in Pink, and Bordering Blue Classic pads; Mellow Moss jumbo cartridge; watercolor brush; Stampin' Dimensionals; Silver cord; Stainless Steel Metal Magic tags

[77 A] Something to Celebrate set; Confetti White and Mauve Mist card stock; Soft Subtles Favor boxes & tags; Basic Black, Barely Banana, Mellow Moss, Mauve Mist, and Bordering Blue Classic pads; watercolor brush; Dazzling Diamonds; linen thread; 1/16" and 1/2" Circle punches; Stampin' Dimensionals; Soft Subtles I eyelets

[77 B] Something to Celebrate set; Mellow Moss, Confetti White, and Mauve Mist card stock; Confetti tag sheets; Basic Black, Barely Banana, Pretty in Pink, and Mellow Moss Classic pads; watercolor brush; Neutrals Fancy Fibers; Stampin' Dimensionals; Dazzling Diamonds glitter

[77 C] Good Times and Great Shapes sets; Bordering Blue, Barely Banana, Ultrasmooth White, and Mellow Moss card stock; Barely Banana and Brocade Blue Classic pads; Love without End Classy Brass template; Stampin' Dimensionals

[78 A] Simply Sweet, All-Year Cheer III, and By Design sets; Creamy Caramel, Night of Navy, Confetti White, and Real Red card stock; Bold Brights tag sheets; Night of Navy, Basic Black, Old Olive, Bordering Blue, and Real Red Classic pads; watercolor brush; Rich Regals eyelets; Red grosgrain ribbon; Notched corner punch; Stampin' Dimensionals; crochet thread

[78 B] Sketch an Event and Contemporary Alphabet sets; Mellow Moss, Night of Navy, Creamy Caramel, and Confetti White card stock; Confetti tag sheets; Night of Navy, Old Olive, and Creamy Caramel Craft pads; watercolor brush; Write Me a Memory Journaling Fonts CD, Volume I; Copper Metal Magic tags, Assortment I; White Square Copper Metal Edge tags; Soft Subtles II eyelets; Natural hemp twine; Spring Moss grosgrain ribbon; 1-1/4" and 1-3/8" Square punches; Stampin' Dimensionals; skeleton leaves; 22-gauge Wire Works; liquid bleach; sewing machine and thread

[79 A] Fun with Shapes and All-Year Cheer I sets; Creamy Caramel, Ultrasmooth White, and Mellow Moss card stock; Soft Subtles and Earth Elements mulberry paper; Old Olive, Yoyo Yellow, Creamy Caramel, and Basic Black Classic pads; Stampin' Dimensionals; Square eyelets; Earth Elements buttons; linen thread; Natural hemp twine

[79 B] Fun with Shapes and All-Year Cheer I sets; Real Red, Mellow Moss, and Ultrasmooth White card stock; Real Red and Mellow Moss Classic pads; White Craft pad; Crystal Effects; Brights Fancy Fibers

[79 C] Fun with Shapes and Simple Type Alphabet sets; Night of Navy, Creamy Caramel, and Real Red card stock; Night of Navy and Real Red Craft pads; Write Me a Memory Journaling Fonts CD, Volume I; Stampin' Dimensionals; Rich Regals eyelets; Natural hemp twine

[79 D] Simply Circles set; Mellow Moss, Ultrasmooth White, and Night of Navy card stock; Night of Navy and Mellow Moss Classic pads; Spring Moss grosgrain ribbon

[80 A] Feathered Friends and All-Year Cheer III sets; Hand-Stitched background stamp; Creamy Caramel, Sage Shadow, Baroque Burgundy, and Confetti White card stock; Confetti tag sheets; Basic Black, Baroque Burgundy, Brocade Blue, Going Gray, Creamy Caramel, Sage Shadow, and Close to Cocoa Classic pads; watercolor brush; Stampin' Dimensionals; linen thread; skeleton leaves; Neutrals buttons

[80 B] Hedgehog Happiness set; Hedgie Play wheel; Brocade Blue, Sage Shadow, and Confetti White card stock; Basic Black, Going Gray, Rose Red, Sage Shadow, Brocade Blue, Creamy Caramel, Close to Cocoa, and Positively Pink Classic pads; Brocade Blue cartridge; watercolor brush; Stampin' Dimensionals; 1/16" Circle punch; Natural hemp twine

[81 A] Framed Greetings set; Brocade Blue, Sage Shadow, Creamy Caramel, and Confetti White card stock; Rich Regals tag sheets; Brocade Blue, Sage Shadow, and Baroque Burgundy markers; Rich Regals eyelets; paper crimper; Subtles Fancy Fibers; linen thread; Stampin' Dimensionals; Soft Subtles buttons

[81 B] Framed Greetings and Tiny Talk sets; Confetti White, Baroque Burgundy, White vellum, Sage Shadow, and Brocade Blue card stock; Basic Black, Sage Shadow, Ruby Red, and Brocade Blue Classic pads; Jet Black StazOn pad; watercolor brush; Stampin' Dimensionals; Bluebird grosgrain ribbon; Stainless Steel Metal Magic tags, Assortment II; crochet thread

[81 C] Little Hellos set; Confetti White and Brocade Blue card stock; Earth Elements Pouch boxes & tags; Basic Black, Creamy Caramel, Brocade Blue, Baroque Burgundy, Sage Shadow, and Barely Banana Classic pads; watercolor brush; Bluebird grosgrain ribbon; Stampin' Dimensionals; Notched corner punch; Rectangle punch

[82 A] Many Moos set; Marvelous Magenta, Old Olive, More Mustard, and Confetti White card stock; Basic Black, Marvelous Magenta, Old Olive, More Mustard, and Going Gray Classic pads; watercolor brush; Stampin' Dimensionals; Earth Elements buttons; linen thread; paper crimper

[82 B] Mini Medleys, Itty Bitty Backgrounds, and All-Year Cheer I sets; More Mustard, Eggplant Envy, Old Olive, and Confetti White card stock; More Mustard, Eggplant Envy, and Old Olive Craft pads; More Mustard and Old Olive Classic pads; Crystal Clear embossing powder; Earth Elements eyelets; Stampin' Dimensionals; linen thread

[82 C] Mini Medleys and Classic Alphabet sets; Easy Check wheel; Old Olive, More Mustard, Ruby Red, and Confetti White card stock; Ruby Red and More Mustard Craft pads; Write Me a Memory Journaling Fonts CD, Volume I; Stampin' Dimensionals

[83 A] Simple Sketches set; French Script background stamp; Ruby Red, More Mustard, and Confetti White card stock; Ruby Red Classic pad; Natural hemp twine; Stampin' Dimensionals

[83 B] A Greeting for All Reasons set; Eggplant Envy, More Mustard, Old Olive, and Confetti White card stock; Basic Black, Eggplant Envy, More Mustard, and Old Olive Classic pads; watercolor brush; White Square Aluminum Metal Edge tags; paper crimper; Stampin' Dimensionals; Silver cord

[84 A] Sketch a Party set; Positively Pink and Summer Sun card stock; Rich Regals Mini Gable boxes & tags; Positively Pink and Ballet Blue Classic pads; Bold Brights eyelets; Stampin' Dimensionals; Yellow Gold grosgrain ribbon

[84 B] Perfect Party and Simple Sayings II sets; Positively Pink, Only Orange, Summer Sun, and Ultrasmooth White card stock; Positively Pink and Summer Sun Classic pads; 1/8" Circle punch; Stampin' Dimensionals; Rose grosgrain ribbon

[85 A] Smile set; Ballet Blue, Yoyo Yellow, Only Orange, and Ultrasmooth White card stock; Yoyo Yellow, Only Orange, and Ballet Blue Classic pads; Stampin' Dimensionals; Love without End Classy Brass template

[85 B] Smile, Smile Some More, and Fresh Fillers sets; Positively Pink, Ballet Blue, Summer Sun, and Ultrasmooth White card stock; Ultrasmooth tag sheets; Positively Pink and Ballet Blue Classic pads; Rich Regals buttons; Basic eyelets; Stampin' Dimensionals; White grosgrain ribbon; crochet thread

[85 C] Surprise! set; Splatter wheel; Ballet Blue, Summer Sun, Only Orange, and Ultrasmooth White card stock; Ballet Blue Classic pad; Ballet Blue cartridge; Bold Brights II eyelets

[86 A] Polka Dot Party and Simple Type sets; White vellum, Rose Romance, Lavender Lace, Creamy Caramel, and Ultrasmooth White card stock; Rose Romance, Creamy Caramel, and Lavender Lace Craft pads; Basic Black journaler; Earth Elements eyelets; Rose grosgrain ribbon; paper crimper

[86 B] Polka Dot Party and Everyday Flexible Phrases sets; Perfect Polka Dots wheel; Ultrasmooth White, Bliss Blue, and Creamy Caramel card stock; Ultrasmooth tag sheets; Creamy Caramel and Bliss Blue Classic pads; Ballet Blue jumbo cartridge; Stampin' Dimensionals; White grosgrain ribbon; 22-gauge Wire Works

[87 A] It's a Party set; Rose Romance, Bliss Blue, Creamy Caramel, and Ultrasmooth White card stock; Rose Romance, Bliss Blue, and Lavender Lace Classic pads; Basic Black marker; Stampin' Dimensionals; Stainless Steel Metal Magic tags; Soft Subtles II eyelets; Silver cord

[87 B] It's a Party and Itty Bitty Backgrounds sets; Bliss Blue, Lovely Lilac, Rose Romance, Creamy Caramel, and Ultrasmooth White card stock; Brocade Blue and Rose Romance Classic pads; Rose Romance, Bliss Blue, and Chocolate Chip markers; Stampin' Dimensionals; paper crimper; Rose grosgrain ribbon; 1/16" Circle punch; 22-gauge Wire Works; White Square Aluminum Metal Edge tags

[87 C] Let's Party set; Simple Stripes background stamp; Orchid Opulence, White vellum, Creamy Caramel, Brocade Blue, Rose Romance, and Ultrasmooth White card stock; Orchid Opulence, Brocade Blue, Lovely Lilac, and Rose Red Classic pads; Brocade Blue marker; Rose grosgrain ribbon; 22-gauge Wire Works; Stampin' Dimensionals

[87 D] Let's Party and Cheery Chat sets; Party Fun wheel; Creamy Caramel, Bliss Blue, and Ultrasmooth White card stock; Ballet Blue and Creamy Caramel Classic pads; Creamy Caramel cartridge; Vellum Square Metal Edge tags; Stampin' Dimensionals; 1/16" Circle punch; Natural hemp twine

[88 A] Flower of the Month and Happy Birthday Frame sets; Sage Shadow, Confetti White, and Cameo Coral card stock; Basic Black, Sage Shadow, Garden Green, and Cameo Coral Classic pads; watercolor brush; White 3/8" organdy ribbon; Stampin' Dimensionals; Earth Elements buttons; sanding blocks; crochet thread

[88 B] Flower of the Month and Happy Birthday Frame sets; Brocade Blue, Sage Shadow, and Confetti White card stock; Pool Party Designer Series paper and vellum; Brocade Blue Classic pad; Natural hemp twine; Square and Soft Subtles II eyelets; Stampin' Dimensionals; linen thread

[89 A] Birthday Bunnies set; Brocade Blue, Cameo Coral, and Confetti White card stock; Basic Black, Going Gray, Brocade Blue, Cameo Coral, Barely Banana, Sage Shadow, Bliss Blue, Creamy Caramel, and Close to Cocoa Classic pads; watercolor brush; White Square Aluminum Metal Edge tags; Stampin' Dimensionals; Natural hemp twine; Soft Subtles II eyelets

[89 B] Tickled Pink set; Pink Flamingo wheel; Cameo Coral, Sage Shadow, and Confetti White card stock; Basic Black, Barely Banana, Cameo Coral, Sage Shadow, and Only Orange Classic pads; Rose Romance cartridge; watercolor brush; Stampin' Dimensionals; Soft Subtles II eyelets; Natural hemp twine; Crystal Effects

[90 A] Happy Birthday Greetings stamp; Brocade Blue, Confetti White, and Rose Red card stock; Rose Red Classic pad; Rose Red Craft pad; 26-gauge Wire Works; Regals beads; Stampin' Dimensionals; White Square Aluminum Metal Edge tags

[90 B] Sweet Treats and Fun Phrases sets; Whimsical Blossoms wheel; Ultrasmooth White and Rose Red card stock; Bold Brights Pouch boxes & tags; Basic Black, Lovely Lilac, Rose Red, and Gable Green Classic pads; Rose Red cartridge; Bold Brights II eyelets; Delphinium grosgrain ribbon; Stampin' Dimensionals; watercolor brush; crochet thread

[91 A] Pretty Princess set; Rose Red, Lovely Lilac, Confetti White, and Gable Green card stock; Confetti tag sheets; Basic Black, Rose Red, Lovely Lilac, Gable Green, Summer Sun, Positively Pink, and Blush Blossom Classic pads; watercolor brush; Delphinium grosgrain ribbon; 22-gauge Wire Works; Bold Brights II eyelets; Stampin' Dimensionals; Dazzling Diamonds glitter

[91 B] Tassel Time and Classic Alphabet Numbers sets; Graduation Day wheel; Rose Red, Brocade Blue, Lovely Lilac, and Confetti White card stock; Basic Black and Brocade Blue Classic pads; Brocade Blue cartridge; watercolor brush; Silver cord; Stampin' Dimensionals; Rich Regals eyelets

[92 A] Wedding Elegance set; Almost Amethyst and Pretty in Pink card stock; Silver metallic pad; Sterling Silver embossing powder; Silver cord; Stainless Steel Metal Magic tags, Assortment II; 1/2" Circle punch; Basic eyelets; Stampin' Dimensionals; Write Me a Memory Journaling Fonts CD, Volume I; Blue 3/8" organdy ribbon

[92 B] Birthday Banter set; Barely Banana, Rose Romance, Pretty in Pink, and Confetti White card stock; Basic Black, Rose Red, Barely Banana, and Pretty in Pink Classic pads; watercolor brush; paper crimper; Small Flower eyelets; Brights Fancy Fibers; Stampin' Dimensionals

[92 C] Birthday Banter set; Bitty Blossoms background stamp; Rose Romance, Pretty in Pink, and Confetti White card stock; Basic Black, Rose Red, and Bliss Blue Classic pads; watercolor brush; Stampin' Dimensionals; White grosgrain ribbon; Rich Regals eyelets; 26-gauge Wire Works; Stainless Steel Metal Magic tags, Assortment I; crochet thread

[93 A] Special Day stamp; Rose Romance, Almost Amethyst, and Barely Banana card stock; Soft Subtles tag sheets; Rose Red and Basic Black Classic pads; Small Flower eyelets; Stampin' Dimensionals; Cream grosgrain ribbon; Regals Magic Mesh; crochet thread

[93 B] Happily Ever After set; Barely Banana, White vellum, Rose Romance, and Confetti White card stock; Basic Black, Rose Romance, Gable Green, and Barely Banana Classic pads; watercolor brush; 1/8" Circle punch; Cream grosgrain ribbon; paper crimper; Stampin' Dimensionals

[93 C] Happily Ever After set; Pretty in Pink, Confetti White, and Rose Romance card stock; Silver Bliss Designer Series vellum; Basic Black, Rose Romance, Gable Green, Almost Amethyst, Blush Blossom, Barely Banana, Bliss Blue, and Close to Cocoa Classic pads; watercolor brush; Notched corner punch; 1/16" Circle punch; Stampin' Dimensionals; Silver cord; Dazzling Diamonds glitter

[93 D] Happily Ever After set; Pretty in Pink and Confetti White card stock; Silver Bliss Designer Series paper; Soft Subtles Favor boxes & tags; Basic Black, Bliss Blue, Rose Romance, and Green Galore Classic pads; watercolor brush; 1/16" Circle punch; Silver cord; Stampin' Dimensionals; Dazzling Diamonds glitter

[94 A] Announcements set; Brocade Blue, Sage Shadow, and Confetti White card stock; Confetti tag sheets; Brocade Blue, Sage Shadow, and Cameo Coral Classic pads; paper crimper; Soft Subtles II eyelets; Stampin' Dimensionals; crochet thread

[94 B] Welcome, Little One set; Sage Shadow, Brocade Blue, and Confetti White card stock; Soft Subtles mulberry paper; Basic Black, Sage Shadow, Brocade Blue, Cameo Coral, Blush Blossom, Creamy Caramel, Barely Banana, and Pretty in Pink Classic pads; watercolor brush; Soft Subtles buttons; crochet thread

[94 C] Welcome, Little One set; Sage Shadow, Barely Banana, Brocade Blue, and Confetti White card stock; Brocade Blue and Sage Shadow Classic pads; Brocade Blue marker; Stampin' Dimensionals; Bluebird grosgrain ribbon; Soft Subtles buttons; Soft Subtles I eyelets; sewing machine and thread

[95 A] Somebunny New and Tiny Talk sets; Simple Stripes background stamp; Sage Shadow, Brocade Blue, Confetti White, and Barely Banana card stock; Confetti tag sheets; Basic Black, Sage Shadow, Creamy Caramel, Going Gray, and Brocade Blue Classic pads; Regals Fancy Fibers; Stampin' Dimensionals; watercolor brush; linen thread

[95 B] Somebunny New set; Brocade Blue, Cameo Coral, and Confetti White card stock; Basic Black, Brocade Blue, Cameo Coral, and Creamy Caramel Classic pads; watercolor brush; Stampin' Dimensionals; Light Blue 3/8" organdy ribbon; Soft Subtles buttons; linen thread

[95 C] Maternal Instincts set; Barely Banana, Brocade Blue, White vellum, and Confetti White card stock; Basic Black, Blush Blossom, Cameo Coral, Brocade Blue, Creamy Caramel, and Barely Banana Classic pads; watercolor brush; Soft Subtles buttons; linen thread

[96 A] Steppin' Style set; Mellow Moss, Confetti White, and Real Red card stock; Confetti tag sheets; Bold Brights Pillar boxes & tags; Basic Black, Real Red, Creamy Caramel, and Mellow Moss Classic pads; watercolor brush; Stampin' Dimensionals; Basic eyelets; Silver brads; Red grosgrain ribbon

[96 B] I Like Your Style set; Swirl Style wheel; Creamy Caramel, Confetti White, Basic Black, and Real Red card stock; Real Red, Basic Black, and Creamy Caramel Classic pads; Real Red cartridge; Basic eyelets; Neutrals buttons; Stampin' Dimensionals; linen thread; Brights Fancy Fibers

[97 A] Definitely Diner and All-Year Cheer II sets; Ballet Blue, Basic Black, Confetti White, and Real Red card stock; Real Red and Basic Black Classic pads; Stampin' Dimensionals; Stainless Steel Metal Magic tags; Red grosgrain ribbon; paper crimper

[97 B] Definitely Diner and Classic Alphabet sets; Ballet Blue, Real Red, and Confetti White card stock; Confetti tag sheets; Ballet Blue and Real Red Craft pads; Basic Black journaler; Basic eyelets; Stampin' Dimensionals; Stainless Steel Metal Magic tags, Assortment I; Blue hemp twine

[97 C] Right at Home set; Real Red, Mellow Moss, Confetti White, and Ballet Blue card stock; Basic Black, Creamy Caramel, Going Gray, Real Red, Mellow Moss, Ballet Blue, Close to Cocoa, and Barely Banana Classic pad; watercolor brush; Stainless Steel Metal Magic tags, Assortment I; Basic eyelets; Natural hemp twine; Stampin' Dimensionals

[97 D] Right at Home set; Hand-Stitched background stamp; Mellow Moss, Ballet Blue, Real Red, and Confetti White card stock; Mellow Moss, Basic Black, Barely Banana, Ballet Blue, Real Red, Going Gray, Creamy Caramel, and Close to Cocoa Classic pads; watercolor brush; Stampin' Dimensionals; 1/8" Circle punch; 22-gauge Wire Works; Red grosgrain ribbon

[98 A] Words by Wanda and Fresh Fillers sets; Ballet Blue, Positively Pink, Pink Passion, Gable Green, and Confetti White card stock; Confetti tag sheets; Basic Black, Ballet Blue, Summer Sun, Pink Passion, Positively Pink, Blush Blossom, Gable Green, and Creamy Caramel Classic pads; watercolor brush; Stampin' Dimensionals; Bold Brights I and II eyelets; 22-gauge Wire Works

[98 B] Espress Yourself, Fresh Fillers, and Classic Alphabet sets; Ballet Blue, Gable Green, Positively Pink, Pink Passion, and Confetti White card stock; Basic Black Craft pad; VersaMark pad; Bold Brights II eyelets; Rose grosgrain ribbon; Stampin' Dimensionals; Write Me a Memory Journaling Fonts CD, Volume I

[99 A] Little Love set; Positively Pink, Ballet Blue, Gable Green, and Confetti White card stock; Vellum Circle Aluminum Metal Edge tags; Basic Black, Positively Pink, Ballet Blue, Chocolate Chip, and Real Red Classic pads; watercolor brush; Apple Green grosgrain ribbon; Stampin' Dimensionals; Bold Brights I eyelets

[99 B] Wanda's Wit & Wisdom set; Ballet Blue, Confetti White, Gable Green, and Positively Pink card stock; Basic Black, Ballet Blue, Creamy Caramel, Positively Pink, Going Gray, Chocolate Chip, Gable Green, and Pink Passion Classic pads; watercolor brush; Bold Brights II eyelets; Brights beads; 26-gauge Wire Works

[99 C] Wanda's Wit & Wisdom and Fresh Fillers sets; Confetti White and Pink Passion card stock; Rich Regals Pillar boxes & tags; Basic Black, Blush Blossom, Really Rust, Pretty in Pink, Pink Passion, Gable Green, Going Gray, and Ballet Blue Classic pads; watercolor brush; Daisy punch; Rose grosgrain ribbon; Silver brads; Stampin' Dimensionals; crochet thread

[100 A] What's for Dinner set; Chocolate Chip, Creamy Caramel, Ballet Blue, Real Red, and Confetti White card stock; Basic Black, Creamy Caramel, Real Red, and Ballet Blue Classic pads; Basic Black marker; watercolor brush; Natural hemp twine; Square eyelets; 1/16" Circle punch

[100 B] What's for Dinner, Shape-Ups, and Simple Sayings sets; Geometric background stamp; Creamy Caramel, Real Red, and Ultrasmooth White card stock; Real Red, Basic Black, and Creamy Caramel Classic pads; Basic Black, Real Red, Going Gray, and Creamy Caramel markers; Stainless Steel Metal Magic tags, Assortment II; 1-1/4" and 1/16" Circle punches; Coluzzle cutting system; Stampin' Dimensionals; Earth Elements eyelets; Black hemp twine

[100 C] Cute Critters and Fresh Fillers sets; Ballet Blue, Creamy Caramel, Real Red, and Confetti White card stock; Basic Black, Real Red, Creamy Caramel, Only Orange, and Ballet Blue Classic pads; White Craft pad; watercolor brush; Silver brads; 1/8" Circle punch; Earths Fancy Fibers

[101 A] Heads Up set; Ultrasmooth White and Chocolate Chip card stock; Pickles Designer Series paper and vellum; Ballet Blue Classic pad; Ballet Blue and Chocolate Chip markers; Square and Large Circle eyelets; Natural hemp twine; Stampin' Dimensionals

[101 B] Heads Up set; Confetti White card stock; Bold Brights Favor boxes & tags; Ballet Blue and Real Red Classic pads; Real Red and Ballet Blue markers; Stampin' Dimensionals; 22-gauge Wire Works

[101 C] Jazzed Up and Great Shapes sets; Jazz wheel; Creamy Caramel, Ballet Blue, Real Red, and Confetti White card stock; Creamy Caramel, Real Red, Ballet Blue, and Chocolate Chip Classic pads; Chocolate Chip cartridge; paper crimper; Stampin' Dimensionals; Natural hemp twine; 1/16" Circle punch

[102 A] Oh So Sweet and Tiny Talk sets; Ruby Red and Confetti White card stock; Soft Subtles Mini Gable boxes & tags; Ruby Red, Mellow Moss, and Close to Cocoa Classic pads; White Square Aluminum Metal Edge tags; Natural hemp twine; Stampin' Dimensionals; Soft Subtles I eyelets; 1/16" Circle punch

[102 B] Oh So Sweet set; Ruby Red, Close to Cocoa, Mellow Moss, and Ultrasmooth White card stock; Mellow Moss and Ruby Red markers; Close to Cocoa Craft pad; Crystal Clear embossing powder; paper crimper; Stampin' Dimensionals; Soft Subtles I eyelets; Taupe grosgrain ribbon; watercolor brush

[102 C] You Warm My Heart set; Mellow Moss, Confetti White, Barely Banana, and Ruby Red card stock; Confetti tag sheets; Basic Black, Ruby Red, Mellow Moss, and Barely Banana Classic pads; watercolor brush; Soft Subtles I eyelets; Spring Moss grosgrain ribbon; Notched corner punch; Natural hemp twine

[103 A] All Natural set; By Definition background stamp; Ruby Red, Confetti White, Close to Cocoa, and Mellow Moss card stock; Confetti tag sheets; Basic Black, Ruby Red, and Mellow Moss Classic pads; watercolor brush; Natural hemp twine; large needle

[103 B] All the Best set; Barely Banana, Mellow Moss, Confetti White, and White vellum card stock; Confetti tag sheets; White Craft pad; Summer Sun and Mellow Moss Classic pad; Natural hemp twine; Stampin' Dimensionals

[103 C] All the Best and Pure & Simple Alphabet Upper sets; Mellow Moss, Ruby Red, and Close to Cocoa card stock; VersaMark pad; window sheets; Stainless Steel Metal Magic tags, Assortment I; Stampin' Dimensionals; Taupe grosgrain ribbon; White Square Aluminum Metal Edge tags; 22-gauge Wire Works; Write Me a Memory Journaling Fonts CD, Volume I; 1/4" Circle punch

[104 A] All God's Children set; Just Jeans background stamp; Bliss Blue, Cameo Coral, Gable Green, and Confetti White card stock; Basic Black, Brocade Blue, Creamy Caramel, Barely Banana, Lovely Lilac, Cameo Coral, Gable Green, Bliss Blue, Going Gray, and Summer Sun Classic pads; watercolor brush; linen thread; needle

[104 B] All God's Children set; Simple Stripes background stamp; Gable Green, Lavender Lace, Cameo Coral, and Confetti White card stock; Basic Black, Cameo Coral, Creamy Caramel, Bliss Blue, Gable Green, Summer Sun, Lovely Lilac, Green Galore, Going Gray, and Chocolate Chip Classic pads; watercolor brush; Stampin' Dimensionals; Light Orchid grosgrain ribbon

[104 C] Little Inspirations set; Lavender Lace, White vellum, Confetti White, and Bliss Blue card stock; Basic Black, Barely Banana, Cameo Coral, and Bliss Blue Classic pads; watercolor brush; White Circle Brass Metal Edge tags

[105 A] Favorite Friends set; Ballet Blue, Cameo Coral, White vellum, and Confetti White card stock; square envelope; Basic Black, Cameo Coral, Green Galore, Barely Banana, Bliss Blue, Lavender Lace, Going Gray, and Pretty in Pink Classic pads; watercolor brush; White Magic Mesh; Gold brads

[105 B] Favorite Friends set; Gable Green, Lavender Lace, Bliss Blue, and Confetti White card stock; window sheets; Basic Black, Bliss Blue, Lavender Lace, Positively Pink, Gable Green, Summer Sun, and Going Gray Classic pads; watercolor brush; Crystal Effects; Soft Subtles II eyelets

[105 C] Paris in the Spring set; Springtime wheel; Cameo Coral, Lavender Lace, Gable Green, and Confetti White card stock; Basic Black, Cameo Coral, Gable Green, Mellow Moss, Lavender Lace, Going Gray, Close to Cocoa, Blush Blossom, and Lavender Lace Classic pads; Mellow Moss cartridge; Stampin' Dimensionals; watercolor brush; Spring Moss grosgrain ribbon

[106 A] Hang in There set; Perfect Plum, Pretty in Pink, and Ultrasmooth White card stock; Slumber Party Designer Series paper; Basic Black, Blush Blossom, Creamy Caramel, Going Gray, Chocolate Chip, Rose Red, and Pretty in Pink Classic pads; watercolor brush; Stampin' Dimensionals; 1/8" Circle punch; 22-gauge Wire Works

[106 B] Charming Children set; Bitty Blossoms background stamp; Perfect Plum, Pale Plum, and Confetti White card stock; Perfect Plum, Blush Blossom, Pretty in Pink, Garden Green, Going Gray, and Close to Cocoa Classic pads; watercolor brush; Oval eyelets; White grosgrain ribbon

[107 A] A New Little Someone, Alphadots, Pure & Simple Alphabet Upper, and Pure & Simple Alphabet Lower sets; Ultrasmooth White and Pretty in Pink card stock; Slumber Party Designer Series vellum; Basic Black Classic pad; Pretty in Pink, Rose Romance, and Going Gray Craft pads; Basic Black journaler; watercolor brush; Stampin' Dimensionals; 1/2" Circle punch; Soft Subtles buttons; 22-gauge Wire Works; crochet thread

[107 B] A New Little Someone and Fun Phrases sets; Wash Day wheel; Pale Plum and Ultrasmooth White card stock; Slumber Party Designer Series paper; Perfect Plum, Pretty in Pink, Going Gray, Pale Plum, and Mellow Moss Classic pads; Coal Black cartridge; watercolor brush; Light Pink 3/8" organdy ribbon

[108 A] Little Engine, Itty Bitty Backgrounds, and Pure & Simple Alphabet Lower sets; Bliss Blue, Baroque Burgundy, Ultrasmooth White, and Night of Navy card stock; Night of Navy, Baroque Burgundy, and Bliss Blue Craft pads; Stampin' Dimensionals; Write Me a Memory Journaling Fonts CD, Volume I; Rich Regals eyelets

[108 B] Baby Firsts and Everyday Flexible Phrases sets; Baby Time wheel; Night of Navy, Bliss Blue, and Confetti White card stock; Confetti tag sheets; Basic Black, Bliss Blue, Blush Blossom, Pretty in Pink, and Night of Navy Classic pads; Jet Black StazOn pad; Bliss Blue cartridge; 1-3/8" Circle punch; watercolor brush; Bluebird grosgrain ribbon; Stampin' Dimensionals; Rich Regals eyelets; Stainless Steel Metal Magic tags, Assortment II; 26-gauge Wire Works

[109 A] I'm Here set; Bliss Blue, Ballet Blue, Night of Navy, and Ultrasmooth White card stock; Ultrasmooth tag sheets; Night of Navy and Ballet Blue Classic pads; Brocade Blue marker; 1/4" Circle punch; Stampin' Dimensionals; Blue 3/8" organdy ribbon; crochet thread

[109 B] I'm Here and Simple Type Alphabet sets; Hand Prints wheel; Night of Navy, Ultrasmooth White, Brocade Blue, and Bliss Blue card stock; Bliss Blue and Brocade Blue Craft pads; Brocade Blue cartridge; Regals Fancy Fibers; Stampin' Dimensionals; 26-gauge Wire Works; Write Me a Memory Journaling Fonts CD, Volume I

[110 A] Crayon Kids and Tiny Talk sets; Just Jeans background stamp; Rose Romance, Barely Banana, Gable Green, and Ultrasmooth White card stock; Ultrasmooth tag sheets; Rose Red and Rose Romance Classic pads; Stampin' Dimensionals; 1/16" Circle punch; 26-gauge Wire Works

[110 B] Crayon Fun and Tiny Talk sets; Ballet Blue, Ultrasmooth White, Gable Green, and Barely Banana card stock; Ballet Blue Classic pad; Ballet Blue Craft pad; Crystal Clear embossing powder; window sheets; Natural hemp twine; Stainless Steel Metal Magic tags, Assortment II; Stampin' Dimensionals; liquid bleach; large needle

[111 A] Teacher Time set; Stipple Plaid background stamp; Ballet Blue, Gable Green, and Confetti White card stock; Basic Black, Ballet Blue, and Chocolate Chip Classic pads; watercolor brush; Bold Brights buttons; Natural hemp twine; Stampin' Dimensionals

[111 B] Buttons, Bows & Twinkletoes, Pure & Simple Alphabet Upper, and Phrase Starters I sets; Rose Romance, Confetti White, Gable Green, and Barely Banana card stock; Green Galore, Rose Romance, Barely Banana, and Going Gray Craft pads; Basic Black Classic pad; watercolor brush; Stampin' Dimensionals; Rose grosgrain ribbon; Write Me a Memory Journaling Fonts CD, Volume I; 1/8" Circle punch

[111 C] Buttons, Bows & Twinkletoes and Simple Sayings sets; Barely Banana, Gable Green, Rose Romance, and Confetti White card stock; Basic Black, Rose Red, Barely Banana, and Gable Green Classic pads; watercolor brush; paper crimper; 1/16" Circle punch; 26-gauge Wire Works; Stampin' Dimensionals

[112 A] Toy Box set; Confetti White, Not Quite Navy, Real Red, and More Mustard card stock; More Mustard, Basic Black, Not Quite Navy, and Real Red Classic pads; watercolor brush; Star eyelets; sanding blocks; Stampin' Dimensionals

[112 B] Dino-Mite and Simple Type Alphabet sets; More Mustard, Old Olive, Not Quite Navy, and Confetti White card stock; Not Quite Navy and Old Olive Craft pads; paper crimper; 1/16" Circle punch; White Square Copper Metal Edge tags; Stampin' Dimensionals

[113 A] Road Trip set; Old Olive, Real Red, Brushed Silver, and Not Quite Navy card stock; VersaMark pad; Basic Black Craft pad; Crystal Clear embossing powder; Stampin' Dimensionals

[113 B] Road Trip and Newsprint sets; Not Quite Navy, Confetti White, Real Red, and More Mustard card stock; Real Red, Not Quite Navy, Basic Back, Going Gray, and More Mustard Craft pads; Write Me a Memory Journaling Fonts CD, Volume I

[114 A] Little Trucks and Simple Sayings II sets; Ballet Blue, Barely Banana, Ruby Red, and Confetti White card stock; Basic Black, Ballet Blue, Barely Banana, Creamy Caramel, Going Gray, and Ruby Red Classic pads; watercolor brush; paper crimper; Bold Brights I eyelets; Stampin' Dimensionals

[114 B] Time for Fun and Simple Alphabet sets; Carnival Fun wheel; Ruby Red, Barely Banana, Ballet Blue, and Confetti White card stock; Vellum Circle Aluminum Metal Edge tags; Basic Black, Ruby Red, Barely Banana, Going Gray, Mellow Moss, Ballet Blue, Blush Blossom, Close to Cocoa, and Pretty in Pink Classic pads; Ruby Red jumbo cartridge; Basic Black journaler; Large Circle eyelets; Spring Moss grosgrain ribbon; Stampin' Dimensionals; watercolor brush

[115 A] Travel Time and Newsprint Alphabet sets; Ballet Blue, Mellow Moss, Ruby Red, and Confetti White card stock; Basic Black Classic pad; Ballet Blue, Going Gray, Ballet Blue, Ruby Red, Summer Sun, Blush Blossom, Creamy Caramel, Pretty in Pink, Chocolate Chip, Mellow Moss, and Bliss Blue Craft pads; Basic Black journaler; Stampin' Dimensionals; watercolor brush; Natural hemp twine; Bold Brights I eyelets; large needle

[115 B] Travel Time and All-Year Cheer II sets; Ballet Blue, Mellow Moss, Ruby Red, and Confetti White card stock; Basic Black, Ballet Blue, Ruby Red, and Barely Banana Classic pads; watercolor brush; Spring Moss grosgrain ribbon; Stampin' Dimensionals; Triangle eyelets

[116 A] Kids at Play and Simple Sayings sets; Brocade Blue, Real Red, Mellow Moss, Night of Navy, and Confetti White card stock; Basic Black, Brocade Blue, Real Red, Blush Blossom, Night of Navy, Close to Cocoa, Chocolate Chip, Bordering Blue, Going Gray, and Mellow Moss Classic pads; watercolor brush; Bold Brights I, Rich Regals, and Soft Subtles I eyelets; Stampin' Dimensionals

[116 B] Kid Cards set; Night of Navy, Real Red, Confetti White, and Mellow Moss card stock; Mellow Moss and Real Red Classic pads; White Craft pad; Night of Navy, Mellow Moss, and Real Red markers; Stampin' Pastels; paper crimper; stamping sponge; 1/16" Circle punch; Stampin' Dimensionals; 22-gauge Wire Works

[116 C] Kid Cards set; Real Red and Confetti White card stock; Soft Subtles Mini Gable boxes & tags; Mellow Moss and Basic Black Classic pads; Mellow Moss marker; Silver brads; 26-gauge Wire Works; Stampin' Dimensionals

[117 A] Girlfriends set; Night of Navy, Brocade Blue, Real Red, Mellow Moss, and Confetti White card stock; Basic Black, Brocade Blue, Night of Navy, Real Red, Going Gray, Close to Cocoa, Blush Blossom, and Mellow Moss Classic pads; watercolor brush; Stampin' Dimensionals; Stainless Steel Metal Magic tags, Assortment I; Blue hemp twine; Basic eyelets

[117 B] Girlfriends and Girlfriends Accessories sets; Real Red, Brocade Blue, Ultrasmooth White, and Night of Navy card stock; Basic Black, Brocade Blue, Real Red, Close to Cocoa, and Bordering Blue Classic pads; watercolor brush; White Circle Aluminum Metal Edge tags; Stampin' Dimensionals; Silver brads; Write Me a Memory Journaling Fonts CD, Volume I

[118 A] Pocket Fun set; Just Jeans background stamp; Eggplant Envy, More Mustard, Old Olive, and Confetti White card stock; Pickles Designer Series paper; Eggplant Envy, More Mustard, and Old Olive Classic pads; sanding blocks; Earth Elements eyelets; Stampin' Dimensionals; watercolor brush

[118 B] Tea Time set; By Definition background stamp; Eggplant Envy, More Mustard, Old Olive, and Confetti White card stock; Eggplant Envy, More Mustard, and Old Olive Classic pads; Stampin' Dimensionals; linen thread; Large Circle eyelets

[119 A] All Wrapped Up, Itty Bitty Backgrounds, and Simple Sayings II sets; Old Olive, More Mustard, and Confetti White card stock; Basic Black, Going Gray, Bliss Blue, More Mustard, and Old Olive Classic pads; watercolor brush; linen thread; Earth Elements eyelets

[119 B] All Wrapped Up, All Wrapped Up Accessories, and Everyday Flexible Phrases sets; Eggplant Envy, Old Olive, More Mustard, and Confetti White card stock; Basic Black, Old Olive, Eggplant Envy, Going Gray, and More Mustard Classic pads; watercolor brush; Stampin' Dimensionals; Silver brads; Spring Moss grosgrain ribbon

[119 C] Totally Cool set; Old Olive, More Mustard, Confetti White, and Eggplant Envy card stock; Confetti tag sheets; Basic Black, Old Olive, Close to Cocoa, Blush Blossom, Rose Romance, Going Gray, Summer Sun, Eggplant Envy, and More Mustard Classic pads; watercolor brush; Stampin' Dimensionals; Olive 3/8" organdy ribbon; Earth Elements eyelets; Regals beads; crochet thread

[120 A] To the Finish set; Brocade Blue, Creamy Caramel, and Confetti White card stock; Brocade Blue, Baroque Burgundy, Going Gray, Basic Black, Summer Sun, Creamy Caramel, and Close to Cocoa Classic pads; watercolor brush; paper crimper; stamping sponges; Silver brads; Natural hemp twine

[120 B] Out of This World set; Brocade Blue, Baroque Burgundy, Confetti White and Creamy Caramel card stock; Creamy Caramel tag sheets; Basic Black, Baroque Burgundy, Sage Shadow, Summer Sun, Brocade Blue, and Creamy Caramel Classic pads; watercolor brush; Stampin' Dimensionals; Rich Regals eyelets; 26-gauge Wire Works

[121 A] Sporting Goods set; Simple Stripes background stamp; Brocade Blue, Creamy Caramel, Baroque Burgundy, and Confetti White card stock; Basic Black, Brocade Blue, Creamy Caramel, and Baroque Burgundy Classic pads; watercolor brush; Stampin' Dimensionals; Neutrals buttons; linen thread

[121 B] Good Sport and Newsprint sets; Creamy Caramel, Baroque Burgundy, and Confetti White card stock; Confetti tag sheets; Pool Party Designer Series paper; Baroque Burgundy and Creamy Caramel Craft pads; Basic Black journaler; Stampin' Dimensionals; sanding blocks; linen thread; Rich Regals eyelets; needle

[121 C] All-Year Cheer II set; Sports Fans wheel; Earth Elements and Rich Regals Pillar boxes & tags; Baroque Burgundy Classic pad; Creamy Caramel jumbo cartridge; Basic Black marker; Earth Elements and Rich Regals eyelets; paper crimper; linen thread

[122 A] Dance Sketches set; Rose Red, Mauve Mist, and Perfect Plum card stock; Eggplant Envy Classic pad; Rich Regals eyelets; Regals Fancy Fibers; watercolor brush

[122 B] Good Sport and Pure & Simple Alphabet Upper sets; Go Team wheel; Rose Red, Eggplant Envy, More Mustard, and Confetti White card stock; Eggplant Envy, More Mustard, and Rose Romance Craft pads; More Mustard cartridge; Write Me a Memory Journaling Fonts CD, Volume I; 1/8" Circle punch; Gold, Red, and Purple hemp twine; large needle

[123 A] Gladsome Garden, Journaling Fun, Phrase Starters II, and Alphadots sets; Posies & Polka Dots wheel; Eggplant Envy, Rose Red, and Confetti White card stock; Rose Red, Garden Green, and Eggplant Envy Craft pads; empty jumbo cartridge; Rose Red ink refill; Eggplant Envy marker; Large Circle eyelets; White grosgrain ribbon; Bold Brights buttons; linen thread

[124 A] Springtime Fun and Alphadots sets; Gable Green, Tempting Turquoise, Green Galore, Orchid Opulence, and Ultrasmooth White card stock; Ultrasmooth pennant sheets; Sassy Designer Series vellum; Green Galore, Tempting Turquoise, and Orchid Opulence Craft pads; VersaMark pad; 1/2" and 1/16" Circle punches; Write Me a Memory Journaling Fonts CD, Volume I; Stampin' Dimensionals; Natural hemp twine

[124 B] Springtime Fun set; Orchid opulence, Ultrasmooth White, Green Galore, and Tempting Turquoise card stock; Green Galore, Tempting Turquoise, and Orchid Opulence Classic pads; Stampin' Dimensionals; 22-gauge Wire Works

[125 A] Buds & Blossoms, Classic Alphabet, and Simple Type Alphabet sets; Bold Blossoms wheel; Green Galore, Tempting Turquoise, Orchid Opulence, and Ultrasmooth White card stock; Sweet Designer Series paper; Tempting Turquoise and Green Galore Craft pads; Green Galore ink refill; empty jumbo cartridge; Stampin' Dimensionals; Bold Brights II eyelets; Write Me a Memory Journaling Fonts CD, Volume I

[125 B] Buds & Blossoms and Everyday Flexible Phrases sets; Orchid Opulence, Ultrasmooth White, Green Galore, and Tempting Turquoise card stock; Basic Black and Tempting Turquoise Classic pads; VersaMark pad; watercolor brush; 1/8" Circle punch; Silver brads; Turquoise grosgrain ribbon; Bold Brights buttons; Natural hemp twine; Scallop scissors

[126 A] Love without End and Tiny Talk sets; Pale Plum, Perfect Plum, Mellow Moss, and Ultrasmooth White card stock; Perfect Plum and Mellow Moss Classic pads; Stampin' Dimensionals; 1/16" Circle punch; 22-gauge Wire Works; Love without End Classy Brass template

[126 B] Watercolor Garden II and Simple Sayings II sets; Perfect Plum, Pale Plum, Mellow Moss, Ultrasmooth White, and White vellum card stock; Perfect Plum, Pale Plum, and Mellow Moss Classic pads; Soft Subtles I eyelets; White 3/8" organdy ribbon; Stampin' Dimensionals; sewing machine and thread

[127 A] Bloomin' Wonderful and Tiny Talk sets; Whirly-Twirly wheel; Perfect Plum, Pale Plum, Mellow Moss, and Ultrasmooth White card stock; Perfect Plum, Pale Plum, and Mellow Moss Classic pads; Perfect Plum Craft pad; Mellow Moss cartridge; Crystal Clear embossing powder; Stampin' Dimensionals; Soft Subtles I eyelets; Natural hemp twine; Stainless Steel Metal Magic tags, Assortment II; large needle

[128 A] Daisy and Newsprint sets; Rose Red, Cameo Coral, and Confetti White card stock; Rose Red, Cameo Coral, and Green Galore Craft pads; Write Me a Memory Journaling Fonts CD, Volume I; Rich Regals Buttons; linen thread

[128 B] Watercolor Minis, Itty Bitty Backgrounds, and All-Year Cheer III sets; Mint Melody, Ultrasmooth White, and Rose Red card stock; Ultrasmooth tag sheets; Bold Brights mulberry paper; Mint Melody, Positively Pink, and Rose Red Classic pads; Light Green 3/8" organdy ribbon; Stampin' Dimensionals; Silver cord; Soft Subtles II eyelets; Silver brads; Stainless Steel Metal Magic tags, Assortment I

[129 A] Exotic Blooms set; Rose Red, Mint Melody, Cameo Coral, and Confetti White card stock; VersaMark pad; Basic Black, Cameo Coral, Mint Melody, Garden Green, and Rose Red Classic pads; Black detail embossing powder; watercolor brush; Stampin' Dimensionals; Green hemp twine; Basic eyelets; liquid bleach

[129 B] Exotic Blooms and Fun Phrases sets; Rose Red and Confetti White card stock; Earth Elements Pillar boxes & tags; Rose Red, Basic Brown, Creamy Caramel, Mint Melody, and Cameo Coral Classic pads; Earth Elements eyelets; Stampin' Dimensionals; Natural hemp twine; watercolor brush

[129 C] Seeds of Kindness set; Dandelions wheel; Mint Melody, Cameo Coral, Creamy Caramel, Rose Red, and Mint Melody card stock; Chocolate Chip Classic pad; Mint Melody cartridge; Earth Magic Mesh; Natural hemp twine; watercolor brush; Stampin' Dimensionals; liquid bleach

[130 A] Stipple Rose and Wonderful Words sets; Hand-stitched background stamp; Mellow Moss, Barely Banana, White vellum, and Naturals Ivory card stock; Basic Brown, Old Olive, Mellow Moss, Close to Cocoa, More Mustard, Barely Banana, and Going Gray Classic pads; watercolor brush; Southwest corner punch; Celery 3/8" organdy ribbon

[130 B] Elegant Rose and Fun Phrases sets; Mellow Moss, Barely Banana, Ultrasmooth Vanilla, and White vellum card stock; VersaMark pad; Old Olive marker; Stampin' Pastels; air art tool; Ivory 3/8" organdy ribbon; spray mount

[130 C] Perfect Petals set; Soft Subtles Pouch boxes & tags; Ultrasmooth White and Mellow Moss card stock; Basic Black, Mellow Moss, Old Olive, More Mustard, and Barely Banana Classic pads; watercolor brush; Soft Subtles I eyelets; 1/16" Circle punch; Rectangle punch; Ivory grosgrain ribbon

[131 A] Roses in Winter set; Confetti White, Perfect Plum, and Pale Plum card stock; Pretty in Pink, Rose Romance, Perfect Plum, Old Olive, Mellow Moss, and More Mustard Classic pads; watercolor brush; Soft Subtles I eyelets; White 3/8" organdy ribbon

[131 B] Heaven Scent set; Perfect Plum, Pale Plum, and Confetti White card stock; Basic Black, Perfect Plum, Old Olive, and More Mustard Classic pads; watercolor brush; Oval eyelets; Stampin' Dimensionals; Soft Subtles Fancy Fibers

[132 A] Terrific Tulips and All-Year Cheer II sets; Gable Green, Orchid Opulence, and Confetti White card stock; Orchid Opulence, Gable Green, and Barely Banana Classic pads; window sheets; Stampin' Dimensionals; micro beads; White 3/8" organdy ribbon

[132 B] Early Spring, Itty Bitty Backgrounds, and Friend to Friend sets; Lilies wheel; Eggplant Envy, Confetti White, and Orchid Opulence card stock; Soft Subtles mulberry paper; Confetti Stationery boxes & tags; Eggplant Envy and Orchid Opulence Classic pads; VersaMark pad; White detail embossing powder; stamping sponges; White Circle Aluminum Metal Edge tags; Orchid 3/8" organdy ribbon; watercolor pencils

[133 A] Simple Florals and Tiny Talk sets; French Script background stamp; White vellum and Eggplant Envy card stock; Ultrasmooth tag sheets; Eggplant Envy, Basic Black, Barely Banana, Bliss Blue, and Green Galore Classic pads; watercolor brush; Soft Subtles I eyelets; Gold 3/8" organdy ribbon; Stampin' Dimensionals; crochet thread; liquid bleach

[133 B] In Full Bloom and Classic Alphabet sets; Bloomin' wheel; Orchid Opulence, Barely Banana, Eggplant Envy, White vellum, and Confetti White card stock; Eggplant Envy, Only Orange, and Orchid Opulence Craft pads; Basic Black Classic pad; Orchid Opulence cartridge; watercolor brush; Soft Subtles I eyelets; linen thread; White Square Aluminum Metal Edge tags; Stampin' Dimensionals; Write Me a Memory Journaling Fonts CD, Volume I

[134 A] Delightful Doodles, Shape-Ups, and Sassy Sayings II sets; Lovely Lilac, Green Galore, Positively Pink, and Only Orange card stock; Lovely Lilac, Positively Pink, Green Galore, and Only Orange Classic pads; Stampin' Dimensionals; Bold Brights buttons; White Square Aluminum Metal Edge tags; sewing machine and thread; crochet thread

[134 B] Fresh Flowers and Tiny Talk sets; Blossoms & Bugs wheel; Green Galore, Only Orange, Positively Pink, Lovely Lilac, and Ultrasmooth White card stock; window sheets; Ultrasmooth tag sheets; Lovely Lilac Classic pad; VersaMark pad; Green Galore cartridge; Crystal Clear embossing powder; Bold Brights II eyelets; 22-gauge Wire Works; Stampin' Dimensionals

[135 A] Build a Blossom, Petite Patterns, and Everyday Flexible Phrases sets; Positively Pink, Green Galore, Ultrasmooth White, and Lovely Lilac card stock; Positively Pink and Only Orange Classic pads; paper crimper; Stampin' Dimensionals; Tangerine grosgrain ribbon; Bold Brights II eyelets; 26-gauge Wire Works; 1/16" Circle punch; Daisy punch; sewing machine and thread

[135 B] Build a Blossom and Sassy Sayings II sets; Positively Pink, Lovely Lilac, Green Galore, and Ultrasmooth White card stock; Lovely Lilac and Green Galore Classic pads

[136 A] Spring Garden and All-Year Cheer III sets; Really Rust, Mellow Moss, White vellum, and Ultrasmooth Vanilla card stock; Really Rust and Mellow Moss Classic pads; Jet Black StazOn pad; watercolor brush; Earth Elements eyelets; 1/2" Circle punch; 3/8" Ivory organdy ribbon; Copper cord; Copper Metal Magic tags, Assortment II; crochet thread

[136 B] Watercolor Garden set; Ruby Red, Mellow Moss, and Confetti Cream card stock; Mellow Moss, Ruby Red, and More Mustard Classic pads; watercolor brush; Ivory 3/8" organdy ribbon

[136 C] Watercolor Garden set; Ultrasmooth Vanilla and Ruby Red card stock; Soft Subtles Pillar boxes & tags; Ruby Red, Bordering Blue, and Mellow Moss Classic pads; watercolor brush; Stampin' Dimensionals; Ivory 3/8" organdy ribbon; Vellum Circle Aluminum Metal Edge tags; 1/16" Circle punch; Soft Subtles I eyelets; Stampin' Dimensionals; crochet thread

[137 A] and Wonderful Words sets; Ruby Red, White vellum, Mellow Moss, and Confetti Cream card stock; Basic Black, Ruby Red, Bordering Blue, Mellow Moss, and More Mustard Classic pads; watercolor brush; Gold brads; Subtles Fancy Fibers; Stampin' Dimensionals

[137 B] Botanicals set; Filigree background stamp; Really Rust, Confetti Cream, Ruby Red, and Mellow Moss card stock; Earth Elements mulberry paper; Basic Black, Ruby Red, Really Rust, Old Olive, and Summer Sun Classic pads; watercolor brush; Stampin' Dimensionals; Earth Elements eyelets

[138 A] Sun-Ripened II and All-Year Cheer I sets; Hand-Stitched background stamp; Close to Cocoa, Mellow Moss, and Naturals Ivory card stock; Mellow Moss, Garden Green, Basic Black, Close to Cocoa, More Mustard, and Barely Banana Classic pads; 1/8" Circle punch; watercolor brush; Ivory 3/8" organdy ribbon

[138 B] Wonderful Wings set; French Script background stamp; Perfect Plum, Really Rust, White vellum, and Naturals Ivory card stock; Rich Regals mulberry paper; Basic Black, Perfect Plum, Ruby Red, More Mustard, and Really Rust Classic pads; watercolor brush; Purple hemp twine

[139 A] Autumn set; French Script background stamp; More Mustard, Close to Cocoa, Naturals Ivory, White vellum, and Really Rust card stock; Soft Subtles tag sheets; Mellow Moss Classic pad; watercolor brush; Earth Elements eyelets; linen thread

[139 B] Lovely As a Tree and Simple Sayings II sets; Perfect Plum, Close to Cocoa, Naturals Ivory, and Mellow Moss card stock; Basic Black, Perfect Plum, Mellow Moss, Garden Green, and Close to Cocoa Classic pads; watercolor brush; Stampin' Dimensionals; Natural hemp twine

[140 A] Pines and Tiny Talk sets; Great Outdoors wheel; Creamy Caramel, Close to Cocoa, Sage Shadow, and Naturals Ivory card stock; Close to Cocoa Classic pad; Jet Black StazOn pad; Close to Cocoa cartridge; Stampin' Dimensionals; Natural hemp twine; Copper Metal Magic tags, Assortment I; Earth Elements buttons; linen thread

[140 B] Pines and Contemporary Alphabet sets; Sage Shadow, Mint Melody, Creamy Caramel, Close to Cocoa, and Naturals Ivory card stock; window sheets; Chocolate Chip, Creamy Caramel, Sage Shadow, and Mint Melody Craft pads; Stampin' Dimensionals; Write Me a Memory Journaling Fonts CD, Volume I Earth Elements buttons; Natural hemp twine; watercolor brush

[141 B] Roughing It and Newsprint sets; Sage Shadow, Mint Melody, Creamy Caramel, Close to Cocoa, and Naturals Ivory card stock; Close to Cocoa, Creamy Caramel, Sage Shadow, and Mint Melody Craft pads; linen thread; Natural hemp twine; Square eyelets; paper crimper; Write Me a Memory Journaling Fonts CD, Volume I

[141 B] Roughing It and Everyday Flexible Phrases sets; Creamy Caramel, Close to Cocoa, Naturals Ivory, and Sage Shadow card stock; Earth Elements tag sheets; Close to Cocoa and Creamy Caramel Classic pads; watercolor brush; Soft Subtles II eyelets; Stampin' Dimensionals; 1/16" Circle punch; Natural hemp twine

[142 A] Ladybug Picnic and Everyday Flexible Phrases sets; Lovely Lilac, Bliss Blue, Confetti White, and Rose Red card stock; Basic Black, Creamy Caramel, More Mustard, Green Galore, Mauve Mist, Lovely Lilac, Going Gray, Brocade Blue, Close to Cocoa, Brocade Blue, and Rose Red Classic pads; watercolor brush; Delphinium grosgrain ribbon

[142 B] Ladybug Picnic and Itty Bitty Backgrounds sets; Rose Red, Lovely Lilac, and Confetti White card stock; Confetti tag sheets; Basic Black, Rose Red, Bliss Blue, Going Gray, Real Red, Gable Green, and Green Galore Classic pads; watercolor brush; Rose grosgrain ribbon; paper crimper; Stampin' Dimensionals; crochet thread

[142 C] Bunch o' Bugs and All-Year Cheer I sets; Dragonfly wheel; Gable Green, Confetti White, and Lovely Lilac card stock; Bold Brights mulberry paper; Lovely Lilac, Bliss Blue, and Green Galore Classic pads; Green Galore cartridge; watercolor brush; Stampin' Dimensionals; Triangle eyelets; Light Blue 3/8" organdy ribbon; paper crimper

[143 A] Bold Butterfly and Pure & Simple Alphabet Lower sets; Flitting By wheel; Rose Red, Brocade Blue, and Confetti White card stock; Lovely Lilac and Rose Red Craft pads; Ballet Blue jumbo cartridge; Basic Black journaler; Stampin' Dimensionals; Light Blue 3/8" organdy ribbon; 22-gauge Wire Works; Regals beads

[143 B] Bold Butterfly and Good Times sets; Gable Green, Bliss Blue, and Ultrasmooth White card stock; Lovely Lilac, Gable Green, Green Galore, and Bliss Blue Classic pads; Small Flower eyelets

[144 A] Cold-Weather Friends, Great Shapes, and All-Year Cheer I sets; Creamy Caramel, Confetti Cream, Close to Cocoa, and Old Olive card stock; Basic Black, Old Olive, Chocolate Chip, Creamy Caramel, and Really Rust Classic pads; watercolor brush; linen thread; Stampin' Dimensionals

[144 B] Yukon and Simple Sayings sets; Creamy Caramel, Close to Cocoa, Old Olive, and Ultrasmooth Vanilla card stock; VersaMark pad; Close to Cocoa Classic pad; Stampin' Pastels; Stampin' Dimensionals; Copper cord; White Square Copper Metal Edge tags

[145 A] Noble Deer and Wonderful Words sets; Creamy Caramel, Old Olive, White vellum, and Close to Cocoa card stock; Creamy Caramel, Old Olive, and Close to Cocoa Classic pads; Natural hemp twine

[145 B] Angler and All-Year Cheer III sets; Creamy Caramel and Taken with Teal card stock; Earth Elements Mini Gable boxes & tags; Earth Elements tag sheets; Old Olive and Taken with Teal Classic pads; paper crimper; 1/16" Circle punch; Natural hemp twine; Stampin' Dimensionals; crochet thread

[145 C] Angler, Classic Alphabet, and Pure & Simple Alphabet Upper sets; Creamy Caramel, Taken with Teal, Old Olive, White vellum, and Ultrasmooth Vanilla card stock; Earth Elements tag sheets; Old Olive, Taken with Teal, Close to Cocoa, Creamy Caramel, More Mustard, and Going Gray Craft pads; Basic Black Classic pad; watercolor brush; Natural hemp twine; 1/16" Circle punch; Earth Elements eyelets; Taupe grosgrain ribbon; Stampin' Dimensionals

[146 A] Wildfowl set; Really Rose, Going Gray, Basic Black, and Confetti White card stock; Basic Black, Going Gray, Bordering Blue, Really Rust, and Taken with Teal Classic pads; watercolor brush; Brass Metal Magic tags, Assortment II; Basic eyelets; Black hemp twine; Stampin' Dimensionals

[146 B] Wildfowl and Simple Sayings sets; Stipple Plaid background stamp; Bordering Blue, Really Rust, Confetti Cream, and Basic Black card stock; Bordering Blue, Basic Black, Really Rust, and More Mustard Classic pads; watercolor brush; Stampin' Dimensionals; Basic eyelets

[146 C] Fantastic Foliage and Simple Sayings sets; Swirling Leaves wheel; Ruby Red and Confetti White card stock; Basic Black, Ruby Red, Only Orange, Close to Cocoa, and More Mustard Classic pads; Ruby Red cartridge; Stampin' Dimensionals; linen thread; watercolor brush; needle

[147 A] Aquaria and Newsprint sets; Ruby Red, Bordering Blue, and Naturals Ivory card stock; Soft Subtles tag sheets; Ruby Red, Mellow Moss, and Bordering Blue Craft pads; Stampin' Dimensionals; paper crimper; Soft Subtles I eyelets; Natural hemp twine

[147 B] Aquaria and Vogue Verses sets; Mellow Moss, Ruby Red, and Naturals Ivory card stock; Basic Black, Bordering Blue, Only Orange, Ruby Red, and Mellow Moss Classic pads; watercolor brush; Neutrals Fancy Fibers; Square eyelets

[147 C] Stipple Shells and Wonderful Words sets; By the Sea wheel; Bordering Blue, Ruby Red, and Naturals Ivory card stock; Soft Subtles mulberry paper; Ruby Red, Really Rust, and Bordering Blue Classic pads; Really Rust cartridge; linen thread; Stampin' Dimensionals

[148 A] Cute As a Bug and All-Year Cheer III sets; Garden Green, Brocade Blue, and Confetti White card stock; Pool Party Designer Series paper; Basic Black, Going Gray, and Brocade Blue Classic pads; Jet Black StazOn pad; Stampin' Dimensionals; watercolor brush; Green hemp twine; Stainless Steel Metal Magic tags, Assortment II

[148 B] Fishy Friends and All-Year Cheer II sets; Sage Shadow, Brocade Blue, White vellum, and Confetti White card stock; Basic Black, Brocade Blue, and Sage Shadow Classic pads; watercolor brush; Natural hemp twine; large needle

[148 C] Fishy Friends and Tiny Talk sets; Fishy wheel; Brocade Blue, Garden Green, and Confetti White card stock; Basic Black, Brocade Blue, and Garden Green Classic pads; Brocade Blue cartridge; watercolor brush; Stainless Steel Metal Magic tags; Bluebird grosgrain ribbon; Basic eyelets

[149 A] Fintastic set; Brocade Blue, Sage Shadow, and Confetti White card stock; Brocade Blue, Basic Black, Going Gray, More Mustard, Sage Shadow, Close to Cocoa, and Blush Blossom Classic pads; watercolor brush; sewing machine and thread

[149 B] Bunch of Bugs and Pure & Simple Alphabet Upper and Lower sets; Brocade Blue, Garden Green, Sage Shadow, and Confetti White card stock; Pool Party Designer Series paper; Confetti tag sheets; Sage Shadow and Brocade Blue Craft pads; Stampin' Dimensionals; White Circle Aluminum Metal Edge tags; Basic eyelets; Natural hemp twine

[150 A] On the Farm and Everyday Flexible Phrases sets; Chocolate Chip, Creamy Caramel, Confetti White, and Mellow Moss card stock; Confetti tags sheets; Basic Black, Chocolate Chip, Creamy Caramel, Going Gray, Mellow Moss, Blush Blossom, Brocade Blue, and Read Red Classic pads; watercolor brush; 1/8" Circle punch; Copper cord; Stampin' Dimensionals; Earth Elements eyelets

[150 B] On the Farm and Newsprint sets; Farmyard wheel; Creamy Caramel, Chocolate Chip, Real Red, Confetti White, and Mellow Moss card stock; Confetti tag sheets; Basic Black Classic pad; Chocolate Chip, Creamy Caramel, Close to Cocoa, Real Red, and Mellow Moss Craft pads; empty jumbo cartridge; Creamy Caramel ink refill; Copper Metal Magic tags; linen thread; Earth Elements eyelets; Taupe grosgrain ribbon; Stampin' Dimensionals; watercolor brush

[151 A] Puppy Love set; Hand-Stitched background stamp; Creamy Caramel, Mellow Moss, Chocolate Chip, and Confetti White card stock; Creamy Caramel, Mellow Moss, and Chocolate Chip Classic pads; VersaMark pad; Earth Tones embossing stack; watercolor brush; linen thread; Stampin' Dimensionals

[151 B] Puppy Love set; Mellow Moss, Chocolate Chip, and Creamy Caramel card stock; Chocolate Chip and Mellow Moss Classic pads; 1/16" Circle punch; Natural hemp twine; Stampin' Dimensionals; liquid bleach

[151 C] Bareback and Wonderful Words sets; Creamy Caramel, Real Red, and Chocolate Chip card stock; VersaMark pad; Earth Tones embossing stack; Classy Copper embossing powder; Silver brads; Taupe grosgrain ribbon; Earth Elements eyelets

[152 A] Something Wonderful set; Perfect Plum, Ruby Red, Barely Banana, and Confetti White card stock; Perfect Plum, Basic Black, Ruby Red, Barely Banana, and More Mustard Classic pads; watercolor brush; Stampin' Dimensionals; paper crimper; Square eyelets; Earths Fancy Fibers

[152 B] In the Wild set; Heart of Africa wheel; Barely Banana and More Mustard card stock; Earth Elements tag sheets; Basic Black, Perfect Plum, Ruby Red, and More Mustard Classic pads; Basic Black cartridge; Basic Black journaler; watercolor brush; Earths Fancy Fibers; Earth Magic Mesh; 1/8" Circle punch

[153 A] Canine Capers and Mini Mates sets; Basic Black and Naturals White card stock; Earth Elements Mini Gable boxes & tags; Basic Black, Ruby Red, Perfect Plum, Gable Green, More Mustard, and Creamy Caramel Classic pads; White Craft pads; Silver brads; Basic eyelets; 22- and 26-gauge Wire Works; Stampin' Dimensionals; watercolor brush

[153 B] Purrfect set; Feline Friends wheel; Ruby Red, More Mustard, Perfect Plum, and Naturals White card stock; Basic Black, More Mustard, Summer Sun, Ruby Red, and Perfect Plum Classic pads; Ruby Red cartridge; Notched corner punch; Stampin' Dimensionals; watercolor brush; linen thread

[154 A] Born to Ride set; Making Tracks wheel; Ballet Blue, Confetti White, and Basic Black card stock; Basic Black and Ballet Blue Classic pads; Basic Black cartridge; Stampin' Dimensionals; watercolor brush; Silver brads; Black hemp twine; Stainless Steel Metal Magic tags, Assortment II

[154 B] Fire Brigade and All-Year Cheer I sets; Real Red, Basic Black, More Mustard, and Confetti White card stock; Basic Black, Real Red, Going Gray, and Bliss Blue Classic pads; watercolor brush; Jet Black StazOn pad; Silver brads; Stainless Aluminum Metal Magic tags; Natural hemp twine; Stampin' Dimensionals

[155 A] Classic Convertibles and Simple Sayings sets; Real Red, Basic Black, and Confetti White card stock; Basic Black, Real Red, Going Gray, and Bliss Blue Classic pads; watercolor brush; Stainless Steel Metal Magic tags; Black grosgrain ribbon

[155 B] Coast to Coast and All-Year Cheer II sets; Simple Stripes background stamp; Ballet Blue, More Mustard, and Confetti White card stock; Confetti tag sheets; Basic Black, Ballet Blue, Real Red, Mellow Moss, Going Gray, Bordering Blue, and Creamy Caramel Classic pads; watercolor brush; Square eyelets; Stampin' Dimensionals; Natural hemp twine

[156 A] The Back Nine set; Night of Navy, Barely Banana, Old Olive, and Confetti White card stock; Basic Black, More Mustard, Close to Cocoa, Old Olive, Night of Navy, Going Gray, Bliss Blue, and Ruby Red Classic pads; watercolor brush; Stampin' Dimensionals; linen thread; stapler

[156 B] Take Me Out to the Ballgame and Everyday Flexible Phrases sets; More Mustard, Mellow Moss, Night of Navy, and Confetti White card stock; Basic Black, Night of Navy, More Mustard, Mellow Moss, Close to Cocoa, and Bliss Blue Classic pads; watercolor brush; Rich Regals eyelets

[157 A] Set Sail set; Old Olive, Night of Navy, and Confetti White card stock; Basic Black, Night of Navy, Old Olive, Brocade Blue, Creamy Caramel, and Ruby Red Classic pads; watercolor brush; Earth Elements eyelets; Natural hemp twine

[157 B] In the Sky set; Night of Navy, More Mustard, Confetti White, and Summer Sun card stock; More Mustard Classic pad; watercolor brush; Gold hemp twine; Stampin' Dimensionals; Brass Metal Magic tags, Assortment II; Rich Regals eyelets; liquid bleach

[157 C] Netherlands and Tiny Talk sets; Hand-Stitched background stamp; Barely Banana, Night of Navy, Confetti White, and Mellow Moss card stock; Basic Black, Night of Navy, Close to Cocoa, Summer Sun, Mellow Moss, and Ruby Red Classic pads; watercolor brush; Rich Regals buttons; crochet thread

[158 A] Stardust set; Naturals Ivory, Night of Navy, and More Mustard card stock; Rich Regals mulberry paper; Night of Navy, Tempting Turquoise, More Mustard, and Ruby Red Classic pads; watercolor brush; Gold cord; Stampin' Dimensionals

[158 B] Beautiful Batik and Classic Alphabet sets; Batik wheel; Ballet Blue, More Mustard, Night of Navy, Real Red, and Naturals Ivory card stock; Real Red Craft pad; Ballet Blue cartridge; Real Red journaler; Stampin' Dimensionals; linen thread; Rich Regals buttons

[159 A] Rhyme Time and All-Year Cheer I sets; Hand-Stitched background stamp; Ballet Blue, Real Red, More Mustard, and Naturals Ivory card stock; Basic Black, More Mustard, Real Red, Night of Navy, Bliss Blue, Close to Cocoa, Going Gray, Bordering Blue, and Pretty in Pink Classic pads; Jet Black StazOn pad; VersaMark pad; Black detail embossing powder; watercolor brush; Stampin' Dimensionals; Gold brads; Creamy grosgrain ribbon; 26-gauge Wire Works; Brass Metal Magic tags, Assortment II

[159 B] Star-Spangled Banner set; Real Red, Night of Navy, and Confetti White card stock; Creamy Caramel and Night of Navy Classic pads; Real Red and Night of Navy markers; watercolor brush; stamping sponges; Stampin' Dimensionals; linen thread; large needle

[160 A] Country Fresh, Simple Sayings, and Background Basics sets; Ruby Red, Bordering Blue, Mellow Moss, and Naturals Ivory card stock; Soft Subtles tags sheets; Ruby Red and Mellow Moss Classic pads; 1/8" Circle punch; linen thread; French Blue grosgrain ribbon; Neutrals buttons; Stampin' Dimensionals; needle

[160 B] Etruscan set; Etruscan Vine wheel; Mellow Moss and Naturals Ivory card stock; Earth Elements mulberry paper; Earth Elements tag sheets; Ruby Red Classic pad; Ruby Red and Old Olive markers; Old Olive cartridge; skeleton leaves; Square and Oval eyelets; Cream grosgrain ribbon; Regals Fancy Fibers; Stampin' Dimensionals; Neutrals buttons; crochet thread; sewing machine and thread

[161 A] Farm Fresh and All-Year Cheer II sets; Hand-Stitched background stamp; Bordering Blue, Ruby Red, Mellow Moss, and Confetti Cream card stock; Brocade Blue, Basic Black, Ruby Red, Mellow Moss, More Mustard, and Close to Cocoa Classic pads; watercolor brush; Soft Subtles I eyelets; Natural hemp twine

[161 B] Farm Fresh set; Stipple Plaid background stamp; Ruby Red, Bordering Blue, and Naturals Ivory card stock; Soft Subtles Mini Gable boxes & tags; Mellow Moss and Ruby Red Classic pads; Stampin' Dimensionals; Neutrals buttons; Natural hemp twine; Gold brads; 1/8" Circle punch

[161 C] Friendship's Journey and Itty Bitty Backgrounds sets; French Script background stamp; Bordering Blue, Mellow Moss, Ruby Red, and Naturals Ivory card stock; Soft Subtles mulberry paper; Basic Black, Bordering Blue, Really Rust, Ruby Red, More Mustard, Mellow Moss, and Blush Blossom Classic pads; VersaMark pad; Bordering Blue marker; Stampin' Dimensionals; Spring Moss grosgrain ribbon; Gold brads; 26-gauge Wire Works; watercolor brush; Earths beads; Gold Glory embossing powder; 1/16" Circle punch; Gold cord

[162 A] Travels Abroad, Itty Bitty Backgrounds, and Classic Alphabet sets; Really Rust and More Mustard card stock; Earth Elements tag sheets; Basic Black, Really Rust, and More Mustard Classic pads; Jet Black StazOn pad; Stainless Steel Metal Magic tags, Assortment I; Silver brads; Triangle eyelets; 1/8" Circle punch; 22-gauge Wire Works; sanding blocks; Black hemp twine; Stampin' Dimensionals; Earths Fancy Fibers; liquid bleach

[162 B] Parisian Plaza, Wonderful Words, Itty Bitty Backgrounds, and All-Year Cheer I sets; Creamy Caramel, Confetti White, and Night of Navy card stock; Rich Regals tag sheets; Night of Navy and Creamy Caramel Classic pads; Rich Regals eyelets; Natural hemp twine; Stampin' Dimensionals; stapler

[163 A] Nostalgia, Elegant Beginnings, and Classic Caps sets; More Mustard, Close to Cocoa, Confetti White, and Creamy Caramel card stock; Earth Elements tag sheets; Tudor Designer Series vellum; Chocolate Chip, More Mustard, Old Olive, Brocade Blue, Really Rust, More Mustard, and Creamy Caramel Craft pads; Basic Black Classic pad; Basic Black journaler; watercolor brush; Ivory 3/8" organdy ribbon; Stampin' Dimensionals; Gold cord; 1/16" Circle punch

[163 B] Thinking of Father set; Night of Navy, Confetti White, and Really Rust card stock; Earth Elements mulberry paper; Basic Black, Night of Navy, Really Rust, More Mustard, Yoyo Yellow, Ruby Red, Going Gray, and Creamy Caramel Classic pads; Jet Black StazOn pad; watercolor brush; Gold brads; Earths Fancy Fibers; 22-gauge Wire Works; Copper Metal Magic tags; Stampin' Dimensionals; 1/16" Circle punch; sanding blocks; Basic eyelets

[164 A] Calming Garden set; Basic Black, Real Red, and Confetti White card stock; Basic Black, Not Quite Navy, Mellow Moss, and Real Red Classic pads; Gold metallic pad; Gold Glory embossing powder; Stampin' Dimensionals; crochet thread and needle

[164 B] Elegant Ornaments and All-Year Cheer I sets; By Definition background stamp; Real Red, Basic Black, and Confetti White card stock; Basic Black and Real Red Classic pads; Black 3/8" organdy ribbon; Stampin' Dimensionals

[165 A] Oriental Brushstrokes and Kanji sets; Basic Black, Real Red, Barely Banana, and Confetti White card stock; Basic Black, Barely Banana, Real Red, Bordering Blue, Mellow Moss, and Creamy Caramel Classic pads; watercolor brush; 1/16" Circle punch; Black hemp twine

[165 B] Oriental Brushstrokes set; Bamboo II background stamp; Basic Black, Real Red, Barely Banana, and Confetti White card stock; Basic Black, Real Red, Barely Banana, Brocade Blue, Mellow Moss, Bordering Blue, and Going Gray Classic pads; Real Red Craft pad; Crystal Clear embossing powder; watercolor brush; Stampin' Dimensionals; Black hemp twine; large needle; skewer; chipboard

[165 C] Kanji set; Barely Banana, Real Red, and Confetti White card stock; White vellum paper; Real Red and Basic Black Classic pads; Stampin' Dimensionals; Rich Regals eyelets; Black hemp twine; watercolor brush; sewing machine and thread

[165 D] Art of the Orient set; Basic Black, Real Red, and Barely Banana card stock; VersaMark pad; White Craft pad; Stampin' Pastels; Black embossing powder; Stampin' Dimensionals; 1/16" Circle punch; Black hemp twine

[166 A] Toile Blossoms and All-Year Cheer III sets; Bordering Blue and Rich Regals Stationery boxes & tags; Ultrasmooth tag sheets; Basic Brown, Creamy Caramel, More Mustard, Mellow Moss, and Baroque Burgundy Classic pads; Rich Regals eyelets; Silver and Wine 3/8" organdy ribbon; Stampin' Dimensionals; watercolor brush; crochet thread

[166 B] Mostly Flowers and Wonderful Words sets; Bordering Blue, White vellum, and Barely Banana card stock; Brocade Blue Classic pad; Stampin' Dimensionals; French Blue grosgrain ribbon; Soft Subtles II eyelets

[167 A] Gentler Times and Wonderful Words sets; Ultrasmooth Vanilla, Bordering Blue, and Baroque Burgundy card stock; Victorian Designer Series paper; Rich Regals mulberry paper; Baroque Burgundy Classic pad; VersaMark pad; Silver detail embossing powder; Stainless Steel Metal Magic tags, Assortment I; Silver brads; Stampin' Dimensionals; French Blue grosgrain ribbon

[167 B] Memory of the Heart and Classic Alphabet sets; Ultrasmooth Vanilla, White vellum, Bordering Blue, and Barely Banana card stock; Victorian Designer Series vellum; Barely Banana, Only Orange, Rose Romance, Old Olive, Bliss Blue, Sage Shadow, Going Gray, and Basic Black Classic pads; Top Boss pad; Basic Black journaler; Timber Brown StazOn pad; watercolor brush; Brass Metal Magic tags, Assortment I; Gold Glory embossing powder; Basic eyelets; Gold brads; Ivory grosgrain ribbon; sewing machine and thread

[168 A] Flora & Fauna and Wonderful Words sets; Bordering Blue, Naturals Ivory, Barely Banana, and Mellow Moss card stock; Soft Subtles and Earth Elements mulberry paper; Basic Black Old Olive, Really Rust, Brocade Blue, and More Mustard Classic pads; watercolor brush; Celery 3/8" organdy ribbon

[168 B] Flora & Fauna, Classic Alphabet, and Contemporary Alphabet sets; Bordering Blue, White vellum, Barely Banana, and Naturals Ivory card stock; Soft Subtles tag sheets; Close to Cocoa, Barely Banana, Summer Sun, Bordering Blue, Bliss Blue, and Mellow Moss Craft pads; Basic Brown Classic pad; Chocolate Chip marker; watercolor brush; skeleton leaves; linen thread; Stampin' Dimensionals; Rich Regals eyelets

[169 A] Swirl Frame Fun and Sassy Sayings I sets; Really Rust, Bordering Blue, and Naturals Ivory card stock; Bordering Blue and Mellow Moss Classic pads; 26-gauge Wire Works; Stampin' Dimensionals; Soft Subtles I eyelets; White Circle Aluminum Metal Edge tags

[169 B] Swirl Frame Fun and Simple Type Alphabet sets; Bordering Blue, Mellow Moss, Creamy Caramel, and Naturals Ivory card stock; Creamy Caramel, Bordering Blue, and Mellow Moss Craft pads; Basic Black journaler; Stampin' Dimensionals; linen thread; 1/16" Circle punch; Earth Elements eyelets

[169 C] Swirl Frame Fun and Everyday Flexible Phrases sets; Swirl Fun wheel; Confetti Cream, Really Rust, and Bordering Blue card stock; Soft Subtles Trapezoid boxes & tags; Confetti tag sheets; Mellow Moss, Bordering Blue, and Really Rust Classic pads; Mellow Moss cartridge; Stampin' Dimensionals; linen thread; Olive 3/8" organdy ribbon

[170 A] Frame & Flourishes and All-Year Cheer II sets; Creamy Caramel and Chocolate Chip card stock; Earth Elements Stationery boxes & tags; Tudor Designer Series vellum; Close to Cocoa and Chocolate Chip Classic pads; 1/16" Circle punch; Ivory 3/8" organdy ribbon; Gold cord

[170 B] Frame & Flourishes and Elegant Beginnings sets; Ultrasmooth Vanilla, Creamy Caramel, and Chocolate Chip card stock; Tudor Designer Series vellum; Ultrasmooth pennant sheets; Creamy Caramel Craft pad; Basic Black journaler; Stampin' Dimensionals; Taupe grosgrain ribbon; Oval eyelets

[170 C] Frame & Flourishes set; Chocolate Chip, Ultrasmooth Vanilla, and Close to Cocoa card stock; Tudor Designer Series paper; Ultrasmooth tag sheets; Basic Black and Chocolate Chip Craft pads; Basic Black journaler; Stampin' Dimensionals; Ivory 3/8" organdy ribbon; Square eyelets

[171 A] Woodland Frame, Elegant Beginnings, and Classic Alphabet sets; Creamy Caramel, Old Olive, and Taken with Teal card stock; Earth Elements tag sheets; Earth Elements mulberry paper; Old Olive, Baroque Burgundy, and Taken with Teal Craft pads; Basic Black journaler; Stampin' Dimensionals; skeleton leaves; Earths Fancy Fibers; Earth Elements buttons; 1/2" Circle punch; Oval eyelets

[171 B] Woodland Frame, Itty Bitty Backgrounds, and All-Year Cheer I sets; Creamy Caramel and Baroque Burgundy card stock; VersaMark pad; Baroque Burgundy Craft pad; Stampin' Pastels; Rich Regals eyelets; Natural hemp twine; Stampin' Dimensionals

[172 A] Shining Star, Pure & Simple Alphabet Lower, and Letter Perfect Backgrounds sets; Lovely Lilac, Real Red, Summer Sun, Ultrasmooth White, and Glorious Green card stock; Lovely Lilac, Real Red, Summer Sun, and Glorious Green Craft pads; Write Me a Memory Journaling Fonts CD, Volume I; Stampin' Dimensionals; Star eyelets

[172 B] Letter Perfect Backgrounds, Mini Messages, and Tiny Talk sets; Real Red, Ultrasmooth White, and Summer Sun card stock; Ultrasmooth and Bold Brights tag sheets; Summer Sun and Real Red Classic pads; window sheets; Yellow Gold grosgrain ribbon; Natural hemp twine; 22-gauge Wire Works; Basic eyelets; Stampin' Dimensionals; sewing machine and thread

[173 A] Fine Frames, Sparkling Summer, and Everyday Flexible Phrases sets; Lovely Lilac, Glorious Green, Real Red, and Ultrasmooth White card stock; Real Red, Basic Black, Bordering Blue, Glorious Green, and Yoyo Yellow Classic pads; watercolor brush; Stainless Steel Metal Magic tags, Assortment II; Delphinium grosgrain ribbon; 22-gauge Wire Works; Stampin' Dimensionals; sewing machine and thread

[173 B] Borders Mini, Tiny Talk, and Buds & Blossoms sets; Lovely Lilac, Summer Sun, Real Red, and Ultrasmooth White card stock; Real Red and Lovely Lilac Classic pads; Stampin' Dimensionals; White Square Aluminum Metal Edge tags; 1/16" Circle punch; crochet thread

[173 C] Yule Bits & Borders and Around & About sets; Real Red, Glorious Green, and Ultrasmooth White card stock; Real Red and Glorious Green Classic pads; Stampin' Dimensionals; Brights Fancy Fibers

[174 A] Itty Bitty Backgrounds and Framed Greetings sets; Rose Red, Cameo Coral, and Confetti White card stock; Basic Black, Rose Red, Rose Romance, and Cameo Coral Classic pads; White Craft pad; Stampin' Dimensionals; watercolor brush; 1/16" Circle punch; 26-gauge Wire Works

[174 B] Stars & Swirls and Sassy Sayings I sets; Creamy Caramel, Confetti White, and Rose Red card stock; Rose Red Classic pad; VersaMark pad; Winter White embossing powder; Stampin' Dimensionals

[174 C] Beyond the Basics, Mini Mates, and Shapes & Shadows sets; Cameo Coral, Rose Red, and Confetti White card stock; Cameo Coral and Rose Red Classic pads; stamping sponge; Stampin' Dimensionals

[175 A] Background Basics, All-Year Cheer II, and Simple Somethings sets; Cameo Cora, Mint Melody, Rose Red, and Confetti White card stock; Rose Red, Basic Black, Cameo Coral, and Mint Melody Classic pads; Basic Black journaler; watercolor brush; Red hemp twine; Stampin' Dimensionals; 1/16" Circle punch

[175 B] Petite Patterns, Lovely Leaves, and All-Year Cheer I sets; Creamy Caramel, Rose Red, Cameo Coral, Confetti White, and Mint Melody card stock; Gold metallic pad; Gold detail embossing powder; Stampin' Dimensionals; skeleton leaves; Natural hemp twine; Brass Metal Magic tags, Assortment I

[175 C] Fresh Fillers and Country Comfort sets; Creamy Caramel, Mint Melody, Rose Red, and Confetti White card stock; Basic Black, Rose Red, Creamy Caramel, and Mind Melody Classic pads; watercolor brush; paper crimper; Silver brads; Stampin' Dimensionals

[176 A] Border Builders and Sassy Sayings II sets; Real Red, More Mustard, Ultrasmooth Vanilla, and Ballet Blue card stock; Mellow Moss, Ballet Blue, More Mustard, and Real Red Classic pads; Stampin' Dimensionals; Spring Moss grosgrain ribbon

[176 B] Smorgasborders and Simple Type Alphabet sets; Ballet Blue, More Mustard, Real Red, and Old Olive card stock; Ultrasmooth tag sheets; Ballet Blue and Real Red Craft pads; Basic Black journaler; Earth Elements eyelets; Red grosgrain ribbon; Stampin' Dimensionals; Bold Brights buttons; crochet thread

[176 C] Itty Bitty Borders and All-Year Cheer III sets; More Mustard, Ultrasmooth Vanilla, Old Olive, and Real Red card stock; Basic Black, More Mustard, Real Red, and Old Olive Classic pads; watercolor brush; linen thread; large needle

[177 A] Great Shapes, Fun Phrases, and Shapes & Shadows sets; Real Red, More Mustard, and Ultrasmooth Vanilla card stock; Real Red, Old Olive, and More Mustard Classic pads; Stampin' Dimensionals; Red grosgrain ribbon; crochet thread

[177 B] Newsprint set; Square Pegs wheel; Old Olive, Ballet Blue, More Mustard, White vellum, and Real Red card stock; White Square Aluminum Metal Edge tags; Ballet Blue Craft pad; More Mustard jumbo cartridge; Basic Black journaler; Stampin' Dimensionals; Spring Moss grosgrain ribbon; Bold Brights buttons; crochet thread

[178 A] Simple Shapes, Tiny Talk, and Favorite Friends sets; Lovely Lilac, Lavender Lace, Marvelous Magenta, and Confetti White card stock; Basic Black, Lovely Lilac, Lavender Lace, and Marvelous Magenta Classic pads; Jet Black StazOn pad; watercolor brush; paper crimper; Stampin' Dimensionals; Delphinium grosgrain ribbon; 22-gauge Wire Works; Stainless Steel Metal Magic tags, Assortment II

[178 B] By Design, Tiny Talk, and Shapes & Shadows sets; Confetti White, Lovely Lilac, Marvelous Magenta, and Almost Amethyst card stock; Bold Brights Pouch boxes & tags; Lovely Lilac Classic pad; Jet Black StazOn pad; Stampin' Dimensionals; Silver cord; Light Orchid grosgrain ribbon; Bold Brights II eyelets; Stainless Steel Metal Magic tags, Assortment II

[178 C] Shape-Ups, Everyday Flexible Phrases, and Gladsome Garden; Almost Amethyst, Lovely Lilac, Lavender Lace, and Confetti White card stock; Bold Brights tag sheets; White Square Aluminum Metal Edge tags; Almost Amethyst, Lovely Lilac, and Marvelous Magenta Classic pads; 1-1/4" Square punch; Stampin' Dimensionals; Delphinium grosgrain ribbon; Bold Brights II eyelets; pencil-top eraser

[179 A] It's a Party set; Dots & Checks background stamp; Almost Amethyst, Confetti White, Marvelous Magenta, and Lovely Lilac card stock; Confetti tag sheets; Lovely Lilac and Marvelous Magenta Classic pads; Stampin' Dimensionals; 22-gauge Wire Works; Delphinium grosgrain ribbon; Silver brads; Basic eyelets; paper crimper

[180 A] Bold Butterfly and All-Year Cheer II sets; Bitty Blossoms background stamp; Perfect Plum, Confetti White, and Really Rust card stock; Perfect Plum Classic pad; Stampin' Dimensionals

[180 B] In the Wild set; On Safari background stamp; Creamy Caramel and Really Rust card stock; Really Rust and Creamy Caramel Classic pads; White Square Copper Metal Edge tags; Copper cord; Stampin' Dimensionals

[181 A] Cheery Chat and Shape-Ups sets; Geometric background stamp; Really Rust and Confetti White card stock; Chocolate Chip, Creamy Caramel, and Perfect Plum Classic pads; Stampin' Dimensionals; Soft Subtles I eyelets

[182 A] All-Year Cheer I and Right at Home sets; Paisley Print background stamp; Lovely Lilac, Bliss Blue, and Confetti White card stock; Basic Black, Lovely Lilac, Real Red, Positively Pink, Bliss Blue, Green Galore, Going Gray, and Creamy Caramel Classic pads; watercolor brush; Stampin' Dimensionals; Silver cord; Silver brads

[182 B] All-Year Cheer II and Something to Celebrate sets; Filigree background stamp; Bliss Blue, Gable Green, White vellum, and Confetti White card stock; Confetti tag sheets; Basic Black, Gable Green, Lovely Lilac, and Bliss Blue Classic pads; Basic Black journaler; Green Galore marker; Stampin' Dimensionals; watercolor brush; 1/2" Circle punch; Soft Subtles II eyelets; Light Blue 3/8" organdy ribbon; sewing machine and thread; crochet thread

[183 A] Cheery Chat, Gladsome Garden, and Itty Bitty Backgrounds sets; Bliss Blue, Lovely Lilac, Confetti White, Gable Green, and Green Galore card stock; Lovely Lilac and Bliss Blue Classic pads; Silver brads; 26-gauge Wire Works

[183 B] All-Year Cheer III and Sweeter Treaters sets; Gable Green and Green Galore card stock; Confetti tag sheets; Bold Brights Pouch boxes & tags; Basic Black, Lovely Lilac, Green Galore, Gable Green, Only Orange, Blush Blossom, Ballet Blue, Creamy Caramel, Only Orange, Summer Sun, Going Gray, and Pretty in Pink Classic pads; Delphinium grosgrain ribbon; Bold Brights II eyelets; Stampin' Dimensionals; Dazzling Diamond glitter; watercolor brush

[184 A] Simple Sayings and Something Marvelous sets; By Definition background stamp; Mauve Mist, Almost Amethyst, White vellum, and Ultrasmooth White card stock; Mauve Mist Classic pad; Almost Amethyst Craft pad; Crystal Clear embossing powder; Blue 3/8" organdy ribbon; 1/8" Circle punch; Silver cord

[184 B] Simple Sayings II and Something to Celebrate sets; Mint Melody, Barely Banana, and Confetti White card stock; Confetti tag sheets; Mint Melody, Basic Black, Almost Amethyst, Mauve Mist, Barely Banana, and Summer Sun Classic pads; watercolor brush; paper crimper; White Circle Aluminum Metal Edge tags; Stampin' Dimensionals; crochet thread

[184 C] Wonderful Words and Summer by the Sea sets; Almost Amethyst, Mint Melody, Mauve Mist, Barely Banana, and Confetti White card stock; Basic Black, Almost Amethyst, Barely Banana, Mauve Mist, Mint Melody, Close to Cocoa, Blush Blossom, and Creamy Caramel Classic pads; watercolor brush; Silver brads

[185 A] Fun Phrases and Happily Ever After sets; Mauve Mist, Almost Amethyst, and Confetti White card stock; Basic Black, Mauve Mist, Almost Amethyst, Mint Melody, Barely Banana, and Blush Blossom Classic pads; White Craft pad; Winter White embossing powder; Bold Basics Classy Brass template; Dazzling Diamonds glitter; Subtles beads; Stampin' Dimensionals; watercolor brush

[185 B] Tiny Talk and Simple Somethings sets; Mint Melody, Mauve Mist, and Confetti White card stock; Basic Black, Almost Amethyst, Barely Banana, Mauve Mist, and Mint Melody Classic pads; White Square Aluminum Metal Edge tags; Stampin' Dimensionals; watercolor brush; Stainless Steel Metal Magic tags, Assortment I; Bold Brights, Neutrals, and Soft Subtles buttons; sanding blocks; crochet thread

[185 C] Vogue Verses set; Geometric background stamp; Ultrasmooth White, Lovely Lilac, and Almost Amethyst card stock; Almost Amethyst and Lovely Lilac Classic pads; White Craft pad; Winter White embossing powder; Stampin' Dimensionals; White grosgrain ribbon; watercolor brush

[186 A] Sassy Sayings I and All the Best sets; Rose Red, Pretty in Pink, Positively Pink, White vellum, and Confetti White card stock; Rose Red Classic pad; Rose Red and Green Galore markers; Bold Brights buttons; crochet thread; needle

[186 B] Sassy Sayings II, Background Basics, and Pretty Princess sets; Lavender Lace, Pretty in Pink, Positively Pink, and Confetti White card stock; Basic Black, Pretty in Pink, Rose Romance, Barely Banana, and Lavender Lace Classic pads; Stampin' Dimensionals; Bold Brights II eyelets; watercolor brush; Dazzling Diamonds glitter

[186 C] Words of Wisdom and Watercolor Garden sets; Pretty in Pink and Confetti White card stock; Positively Pink and Gable Green Classic pads; watercolor brush; Light Pink 3/8" organdy ribbon; sewing machine and thread

[187 A] Brighter Tomorrow and In Full Bloom sets; Rose Red, Pretty in Pink, and Confetti White card stock; Basic Black, Gable Green, and Rose Red Classic pads; watercolor brush; Natural hemp twine

[187 B] Elegant Greetings and Daisy sets; Simple Stripes background stamp; Lavender Lace, Confetti White, and Gable Green card stock; Lavender Lace, Gable Green, and Green Galore Classic pads; Stampin' Dimensionals; Light Orchid grosgrain ribbon

[188 A] Sparkling Summer and Versatile Verses sets; Gable Green, Confetti White, Rose Red, Barely Banana, and Bliss Blue card stock; Basic Black, Green Galore, Rose Red, Barely Banana, and Bliss Blue Classic pads; watercolor brush; 26-gauge Wire Works; Brights beads; Apple Green grosgrain ribbon

[188 B] Bold & Basic Greetings and Fun with Shapes sets; Barely Banana, Gable Green, Bliss Blue, and Ultrasmooth White card stock; Bliss Blue and Barely Banana Classic pads; Bliss Blue Craft pad; watercolor brush

[189 A] Birthday Greetings set; Confetti Play wheel; Bliss Blue, Ultrasmooth White, Gable Green, and Barely Banana card stock; Soft Subtles tag sheets; Bliss Blue, Gable Green, and Barely Banana Classic pads; Clear embossing cartridge; Crystal Clear embossing powder; 1/2" and 1/8" Circle punches; Soft Subtles I and II eyelets; Stampin' Dimensionals; watercolor brush; stamping sponges; Subtles Fancy Fibers

[189 B] Saludos and Let's Party sets; Square Pegs wheel; Bliss Blue, Brocade Blue; Rose Red, and Ultrasmooth White card stock; Soft Subtles tag sheets; Bliss Blue, Gable Green, Rose Red, and Yoyo Yellow Classic pads; Brocade Blue jumbo cartridge; Stampin' Dimensionals; Stainless Steel Metal Magic tags; Regals Fancy Fibers; 22-gauge Wire Works; paper crimper; Square eyelets; 1/16" Circle punch

[190 A] Business Memos set; Positively Pink card stock; Soft Subtles Trapezoid boxes & tags; Positively Pink, Pretty in Pink, and Lavender Lace Craft pads; Heart eyelets; White Square Aluminum Metal Edge tags; Soft Subtles I and Bold Brights II eyelets; Rose grosgrain ribbon

[190 B] Handmade with Love set; Ultrasmooth White, Positively Pink, and Orchid Opulence card stock; Positively Pink and Orchid Opulence Classic pads; Stampin' Dimensionals; 1/8" Circle punch; Brights Fancy Fibers

[190 C] Handmade with Love II set; Positively Pink card stock; Orchid Opulence Classic pad

[191 A] Word Play and Pure & Simple Alphabet Lower sets; Confetti Play wheel; Lavender Lace, Ultrasmooth White, Pretty in Pink, Positively Pink, and Only Orange card stock; window sheets; Only Orange, Lavender Lace, and Positively Pink Craft pads; embossing cartridge; Winter White embossing powder; Bold Brights II eyelets; Stampin' Dimensionals; Write Me a Memory Journaling Fonts CD, Volume I

[191 B] Love without End set; Wonderful wheel; Lavender Lace, Pretty in Pink, and Ultrasmooth White card stock; Lavender Lace, Pretty in Pink, and Lovely Lilac Classic pads; Pretty in Pink jumbo cartridge; paper crimper; 22-gauge Wire Works Crystal Effects; Stampin' Dimensionals

[192 A] Friend to Friend and Stardust sets; Brocade Blue, Baroque Burgundy, and Confetti White card stock; Basic Black, Brocade Blue, More Mustard, Night of Navy, and Baroque Burgundy Classic pads; watercolor brush; Stampin' Dimensionals

[192 B] Season's Greetings and Holiday Sweets sets; Creamy Caramel, Sage Shadow, Baroque Burgundy, and Confetti White card stock; Basic Black, Creamy Caramel, Baroque Burgundy, Sage Shadow, and More Mustard Classic pads; watercolor brush

[194 A] Journaling Fun, Simply Circles, Everyday Flexible Phrases, and Newsprint sets; Confetti White, Ruby Red, Bordering Blue, Eggplant Envy, and Mellow Moss card stock; Ruby Red, Bordering Blue, Mellow Moss, and Eggplant Envy Craft pads; Basic Black journaler; Stampin' Dimensionals; Stainless Aluminum Metal Magic tags, Assortment II; Rich Regals eyelets; Natural hemp twine

[194 B] Journaling Fun, Pure & Simple Alphabet Upper and Lower, Shapes & Shadows, and Phrase Starters II sets; Mellow Moss, Confetti White, Ruby Red, Bordering Blue, and Eggplant Envy card stock; Confetti tag sheets; Ruby Red, Eggplant Envy, Mellow Moss, and Bordering Blue Craft pads; Basic Black journaler; 1/4" Circle punch; Stampin' Dimensionals; Basic eyelets; Natural hemp twine

[195 A] Everyday Flexible Phrases and Stipple Celebrations sets; Perfect Plum, Ruby Red, Mellow Moss, and Confetti White card stock; White Square Aluminum Metal Edge tags; Bordering Blue, Perfect Plum, Mellow Moss, and Ruby Red Classic pads; Silver cord; Silver brads; Stampin' Dimensionals

[204 A] Everyday Flexible Phrases set; Dots & Checks background stamp; Silver pad; Rich Regals Party Favor boxes & tags; velveteen paper assortment; Star eyelets; Silver cord; stamping sponge

[204 B] Carved & Candlelit and All-Year Cheer III sets; Gable Green, Orchid Opulence, Only Orange, and Ultrasmooth White card stock; Only Orange, Gable Green, Green Galore, and Basic Black Classic pads; Stampin' Dimensionals; Subtles Magic Mesh

[205 A] Happily Ever After set; Sage Shadow, Radiant White, and Ultrasmooth White card stock; White and Bold Brights mulberry paper; Basic Black, Blush Blossom, Pretty in Pink, Creamy Caramel, Rose Red, and Sage Shadow Classic pads; watercolor brush; Dazzling Diamonds glitter; Stampin' Dimensionals; White 3/8" organdy ribbon; sewing machine and thread

[206 A] Alphadots and Little Layers sets; Lovely Ladybugs wheel; Barely Banana, Cameo Coral, and Basic Black card stock; Square vellum and Cameo Coral Classic pads; Basic Black cartridge; Stampin' Dimensionals; Write Me a Memory Journaling Fonts CD, Volume II; Subtles Fancy Fibers; watercolor brush; 1/2" Circle punch

[207 A] Love without End and Bold Alphabet sets; Barely Banana, Orchid Opulence, and Ultrasmooth White card stock; Barely Banana, Orchid Opulence, and Mellow Moss Classic pads; sponge brayer; Soft Subtles buttons; Write Me a Memory Journaling Fonts CD; Small Plaidmaker; Stampin' Dimensionals; crochet thread

[207 B] Nice & Narrow set; By Definition background stamp; Mellow Moss, Confetti Tan, and Confetti White card stock; Confetti tag sheets; Pool Party Designer Series paper; Creamy Caramel and Brocade Blue Classic pads; stamping sponges; 1/8" Circle punch; Silver brads; Linen thread; sanding blocks; sewing machine and thread

[208 A] Wonderful Words and Buds & Blossoms sets; Night of Navy and Ultrasmooth White card stock; Copper Bliss Designer Series paper and vellum; Night of Navy Classic pad; VersaMark pad; Vellum Circle Copper Metal Edge Tags; Copper cord; Gold brads; Classy Copper embossing powder; Stampin' Dimensionals

[208 B] All the Best set; Ultrasmooth White card stock; Rich Regals Pouch boxes & tags; Copper Bliss Designer Series vellum; Night of Navy Classic pad; VersaMark pad; Classy Copper embossing powder; Gold brads; Copper cord

[212 A] Simple Type Alphabet set; Quick Strips Simply Scrappin'; Ultrasmooth tag sheets; Slumber Party Designer Series paper; Perfect Plum Craft pad; Basic Black journaler; Light Pink grosgrain ribbon; Stampin' Dimensionals; Write Me a Memory Journaling Fonts CD, Volume I

[212 B] A New Little Someone Boy Simply Scrappin'; Stampin' Dimensionals; Bluebird grosgrain ribbon; Soft Subtles buttons; Write Me a Memory Journaling Fonts CD, Volume II

[212 C] Simple Type Alphabet set; A New Little Someone Girl Simply Scrappin'; Rose Romance Craft pad; Stampin' Dimensionals; 3/8" Light Pink organdy ribbon ; Write Me a Memory Journaling Fonts CD, Volume I

[213 A] Newsprint set; Polka Dot Party Simply Scrappin'; Ballet Blue Craft pad; Ballet Blue journaler; Stampin' Dimensionals; Rose grosgrain ribbon; Bold Brights buttons

[213 B] Alphadots set; Time for Fun Simply Scrappin'; Real Red Craft pad; Basic Black journaler; Stampin' Dimensionals; 1/2" Circle punch

[213 C] Classic Alphabet and Newsprint sets; Buttons, Bows & Twinkletoes Simply Scrappin'; Rose Romance Craft pad; Soft Subtles I eyelets; Subtles fibers; Stampin' Dimensionals; Write Me a Memory Journaling Fonts CD

[214 A] Pure & Simple Alphabet Upper set; Campout Simply Scrappin'; Chocolate Chip Craft pad; Basic Black journaler; Stampin' Dimensionals; Natural hemp twine; Natural Magic Mesh; 1/16" Circle punch

[214 B] Newsprint and Pure & Simple Alphabet Upper sets; Toy Box Simply Scrappin'; Old Olive and Not Quite Navy Craft pads; 1/16" Circle punch; Stampin' Dimensionals; Natural hemp; sewing machine and thread

[214 C] Pure & Simple Alphabet Lower and Classic Alphabet sets; Summer Sketches Simply Scrappin'; Perfect Plum Craft pad; Soft Subtles buttons; Natural hemp twine

[215 A] Classic Alphabet and Classic Alphabet Numbers sets; Travel Time Simply Scrappin'; Real Red Craft pad; Natural hemp twine; 1/8" Circle punch; Stampin' Dimensionals; Write Me a Memory Journaling Fonts CD, Volume I

[215 B] Classic Alphabet set; Vintage Keepsakes Simply Scrappin'; Creamy Caramel Craft pad; Basic Black journaler; Stampin' Dimensionals; Cream grosgrain ribbon; 1/8" Circle punch

[215 C] Pure & Simple Alphabet Upper and Lower and Simple Type sets; Sparkling Holiday Simply Scrappin'; Night of Navy and Old Olive Craft pads; Stampin' Dimensionals; Write Me a Memory Journaling Fonts CD, Volume I; sewing machine and thread

[216 A] Everyday Flexible Phrases sets; Ultrasmooth White card stock; Basic Black Classic pad; magnetic sheets

[216 B] Totally Cool set; Positively Pink, Only Orange, and Confetti Cream card stock; Sassy Designer Series paper; Summer Sun, Basic Black, Only Orange, positively Pink, Pink Passion, and Blush Blossom Classic pads; watercolor brush; vinyl checkbook cover

[216 C] Thinking of Father set; Simple Stripes background stamp; Close to Cocoa and Naturals Ivory card stock; Earth Elements mulberry paper; Chocolate Chip and Creamy Caramel Classic pads; stamping sponge; vinyl checkbook cover

[216 D] Simply Circles and All-Year Cheer III sets; Gable Green, Old Olive, Green Galore, and Ballet Blue Classic pads; memo cube; White Circle Aluminum Metal Edge Tags; 1/8" Circle punch; Bluebird grosgrain ribbon; crochet thread

[216 E] I'm Here set; Ballet Blue and Ultrasmooth White card stock; White vellum card stock; Bliss Blue Classic pad; Jet Black StazOn pad; window sheets; Stampin' Dimensionals; Soft Subtles buttons; White 3/8" organdy ribbon; crochet thread; sewing machine and thread

[216 F] Word Play and All-Year Cheer II sets; Celebration Spectrum pad; Pink Passion, Only Orange, Brilliant Blue, and Lavender Lace markers

[216 G] Shapes & Shadows, Classic Alphabet, and Classic Alphabet Numbers sets; Brocade Blue, Ruby Red, Mellow Moss, Creamy Caramel, and Confetti White card stock; Confetti tag sheets; 6 x 6 Days-to-Remember calendar; Close to Cocoa and White Craft pads; Basic Black journaler; Stampin' Dimensionals; Natural hemp twine; Silver brads; sewing machine and thread

[217 A] Sassy Sayings I and Shapes & Shadows sets; Gable Green, Only Orange, and Pink Passion card stock; Pink Passion, Only Orange, and Gable Green Craft pads; Green Galore Classic pad; White Polyshrink; sanding blocks

[217 B] Shapes & Shadows and Tiny Talk sets; Barely Banana, Brocade Blue, and Real Red Card pads; Summer Sun and Craft pads; Summer Sun Classic pad; Ballet Blue marker; Sculpey; Stampin' Dimensionals; 26-gauge Wire Works; Red grosgrain ribbon; Bold Brights I eyelets; paper crimper;1-3/8" Square punch

[217 C] Definitely Diner and Tiny Talk sets; Old Olive, Confetti White, and Night of Navy card stock; Confetti White circle gift tags; Night of Navy Classic pad; 1/16" and 1/2" Circle punches; Stampin' Dimensionals; Natural hemp; Red grosgrain ribbon; Large Circle eyelets

[217 D] Contemporary Alphabet and Steppin' Style sets; Confetti White door hangers & tags; Basic Black, Pink Passion, Only Orange, Green Galore, and Yoyo Yellow Classic pads; watercolor brush

[217 E] Pocket Fun and All-Year Cheer I sets; Confetti White door hangers & tags; Pretty in Pink, More Mustard, and Brocade Blue Classic pads; VersaMark pad; Crystal Clear embossing powder; Large Circle eyelets; White 3/8" organdy ribbon; stamping sponges

[217 F] It's a Party set; Ultrasmooth White, Brocade Blue, and Sage Shadow card stock; Pool Party Designer Series paper; Ultrasmooth White large bookmarks; Sage Shadow and Brocade Blue Classic pads; Brocade Blue marker; Subtles embossing stack; Stampin' Dimensionals; 22-gauge Wire Works; Square eyelets; 1/2" Circle punch; French Blue grosgrain ribbon

[217 G] Shapes & Shadows and Sassy Sayings II sets; Ultrasmooth White and Positively Pink card stock; Ultrasmooth White door hanger pouch; Positively Pink, Gable Green, and Lavender Lace Classic pads; Bold Brights II eyelets; Rose grosgrain ribbon

[218 A] In Full Bloom and Everyday Flexible Phrases sets; Confetti White and Creamy Caramel card stock; Earth Elements tag sheets; Basic Black, Creamy Caramel, Garden Green, and Ruby Red Classic pads; Natural Magic Mesh; linen thread; Natural hemp twine; Stampin' Dimensionals; Square eyelets; Vellum Square Copper Metal Edge tags; watercolor brush

[218 B] In Full Bloom and Wonderful Words sets; Ruby Red, Close to Cocoa, and Creamy Caramel card stock; Earth Elements vellum; Close to Cocoa Classic pad; VersaMark pad; Classy Copper embossing powder; Copper Metal Magic tags; Assortment I; Gold brads; Earths Fancy Fibers; Stampin' Dimensionals; needle

[219 A] Newsprint set; By Definition background stamp; Rich Regals tag sheets; Night of Navy and Creamy Caramel Classic pads; VersaMark pad; Stampin' Pastels; Silver brad; paper crimper; Natural hemp; stamping sponges; Stampin' Dimensionals

[219 B] Little Hellos set; Soft Subtles tag sheets; Basic Black, Pretty in Pink, Baroque Burgundy, Mellow Moss, and Bliss Blue Classic pads; watercolor brush; scallop scissors; Spring Moss and Light Pink grosgrain ribbon

[219 C] Basic Black marker; Regal Tones fibers; Rich Regals eyelets; Stampin' Dimensionals; 1-3/8" Square punch

[219 D] Letter Perfect Backgrounds, Classic Alphabet, and Contemporary Alphabet sets; Night of Navy, Gable Green, Barely Banana, and Ultrasmooth White card stock; Rich Regals pennant sheets; Gable Green, Barely Banana, Night of Navy, and White Craft pads; Night of Navy marker; Write Me a Memory Journaling Fonts CD; Gold brads; White Circle Brass Metal Edge Tags; 1/16" Circle punch; Soft Subtles I eyelets; Natural hemp; Stampin' Dimensionals; paper crimper

[219 E] Pines set; Earth Elements and Soft Subtles Party Favor boxes & tags; Mellow Moss and Chocolate Chip Classic pads; Linen thread; Stampin' Dimensionals

[219 F] Shapes & Shadows and Itty Bitty Backgrounds sets; Creamy Caramel and Mellow Moss card stock; Earth Elements Trapezoid boxes & tags; Creamy Caramel, Mellow Moss, Ruby Red, and Close to Cocoa Classic pads; Stampin' Dimensionals; 1/8" Circle punch; Natural hemp

[220 A] In Full Bloom set; Night of Navy and Confetti White card stock; Earth Elements Pillar boxes & tags; Close to Cocoa, Ruby Red, Chocolate Chip, Basic Black, and Old Olive Classic pads; watercolor brush; 1/8" Circle punch; Linen thread

[220 B] Buds & Blossoms and All-Year Cheer II sets; Confetti White and Confetti Tan card stock; Soft Subtles Mini Gable boxes & tags; Night of Navy, Real Red, and Mellow Moss Classic pads; paper crimper; Taupe grosgrain ribbon; Linen thread; Earth Elements eyelets; Stampin' Dimensionals; 1/8" Circle punch

[220 C] Aquaria set; Ruby Red and Confetti White card stock; Rich Regals Stationery boxes & tags; Basic Black, Night of Navy, Ruby Red, and Mellow Moss Classic pads; White Circle Aluminum Metal Edge tags; Stampin' Dimensionals; Natural hemp twine; Crystal Effects; Spring Moss grosgrain ribbon; watercolor brush

[220 D] Wonderful Words and Watercolor Garden II sets; Confetti Pouch boxes & tags; Ruby Red, Mellow Moss, and Creamy Caramel Classic pads; Ivory and Olive 3/8" organdy ribbon; Earth Elements eyelets; Linen thread; Stampin'

[220 E] Mini Mates set; Square Pegs wheel; Real Red, Not Quite Navy, Old Olive, and Ultrasmooth White card stock; Earth Elements Pillar boxes & tags; Real Red and Not Quite Navy Classic pads; jumbo empty cartridge; Old Olive ink refill; Bold Brights I and Earth Elements eyelets; watercolor brush

[221 A] Gladsome Garden and Everyday Flexible Phrases sets; Ultrasmooth Vanilla, Mellow Moss, and Not Quite Navy card stock; Baroque Burgundy and Mellow Moss Craft pads; Jet Black StazOn pad; VersaMark pad; Medium Kraft Gable box; Stampin' Dimensionals; Stainless Steel Metal Magic Tags Assortment I; Soft Subtles I eyelets; Natural hemp; paper crimper; sewing machine and thread

[221 B] Spring Fling set; Ultrasmooth tag sheets; Lavender Lace Classic pad; VersaMark pad; medium organdy bag; Subtles embossing stack; Ivory 3/8" organdy ribbon

[225 A] Yule Bits & Borders set; More Mustard, Real Red, Garden Green, and Ultrasmooth Vanilla card stock; More Mustard and Real Red Craft pads; VersaMark pad; Brights embossing stack; Gold brads; Tearing Edge; Stampin' Dimensionals; Gold cord; sewing machine and thread

[226 A] Shapes & Shadows and Everyday Flexible Phrases sets; Pink Passion, Marvelous Magenta, Ultrasmooth White, and Lavender Lace card stock; Marvelous Magenta Classic pad; Parfait Spectrum pad; White Square Aluminum Metal Edge tags; Stampin' Dimensionals

[226 B] Shapes & Shadows set; By Definition background stamp; Ruby Red, Old Olive, More Mustard, and Perfect Plum, card stock; Confetti tag sheets; VersaMark pad; Stampin' Dimensionals; 22-gauge Wire Works; Stainless Steel Metal Magic tags, Assortment I; Basic eyelets; Natural hemp twine; stamping sponge; 1/4" Circle punch; sewing machine and thread

[227 A] In Full Bloom and Everyday Flexible Phrases sets; Marvelous Magenta; Lovely Lilac, Confetti White, and Summer Sun card stock; Lovely Lilac and Basic Black Classic pads; watercolor brush; watercolor pencils; White 3/8" organdy ribbon; Bold Brights II eyelets; Stampin' Dimensionals; Stainless Steel Metal Magic Tags Assortment II; crochet thread

[228 A] Newsprint set; Night of Navy card stock; White Craft pad

[230 A] Simply Circles set; Only Orange, Positively Pink, and Ultrasmooth White card stock; VersaMark pad; Only Orange and Positively Pink Classic pads; Crystal Clear embossing powder; stamping sponges; Bold Brights II eyelets

[231 A] Green Galore, Positively Pink, and Lavender Lace card stock; Love without End brass template; Positively Pink, Green Galore, Lovely Lilac, and Only Orange eyelets; Light Orchid grosgrain ribbon; Large and Small corner rounder punches

[232 A] Sparkling Summer and Good Times sets; Simple Stripes background stamp; Gable Green, Bliss Blue, and Confetti White card stock; Basic Black, Cameo Coral, Green Galore, Bliss Blue, and More Mustard; VersaMark pad; Heat & Stick powder; Dazzling Diamonds glitter; Apple Green grosgrain ribbon; 22-gauge Wire Works; Stainless Steel Metal Magic tags, Assortment II; Stampin' Dimensionals; watercolor brush

[232 B] Lovely as a Tree set; Night of Navy, Brushed Silver, and Brushed Gold card stock; Lumiere; Pearl Ex, Assortment I and II; Silver brads; watercolor brush

[232 C] Love without End set; Positively Pink, Gable Green, and Confetti White card stock; Only Orange, Positively Pink, and Green Galore Classic pads; Rose grosgrain ribbon; Stampin' Dimensionals; Crystal Effects; 22-gauge Wire Works; Square Aluminum Metal Edge Tags; Linen thread; needle

[234 A] All Natural set; Creamy Caramel, Close to Cocoa, Ruby Red, and Naturals Ivory card stock; Creamy Caramel, Close to Cocoa, and ruby Red Classic pads; skeleton leaves; Square Copper Metal Edge Tags; Stampin' Dimensionals; Earth Elements buttons; Linen thread; stamping sponge

[234 B] Jazzed Up set; Lovely Lilac, Ballet Blue, Ultrasmooth White, and More Mustard card stock; Lovely Lilac, Ballet Blue, and More Mustard Classic pads; watercolor brush; Stampin' Dimensionals; 26-gauge Wire Works

[234 C] Totally Cool set; Gable Green, Only Orange, Green Galore, Confetti White, and Yoyo Yellow card stock; Basic Black, Yoyo Yellow, Summer Sun, Green Galore, Creamy Caramel, Chocolate Chip, Pretty in Pink, Rose Romance, Blush Blossom, and Gable Green Classic pads; watercolor brush; Bright beads; 26-gauge Wire Works; Stampin' Dimensionals; White grosgrain ribbon

[234 D] All the Best set; Bliss Blue, Creamy Caramel, and Confetti White card stock; Creamy Caramel Bliss Blue, and Pretty in Pink Classic pads; Soft Subtles buttons; Linen thread; Stampin' Dimensionals; sewing machine and thread

[235 A] Fun with Shapes and Everyday Flexible Phrases sets; Close to Cocoa, Ultrasmooth White, and More Mustard card stock; Soft Subtles tag sheets; Mellow Moss, More Mustard, and Close to Cocoa Classic pads; Stampin' Dimensionals; Earth Elements eyelets; Natural hemp; Brights and White Magic Mesh